Singular systems of differential equations

S L Campbell

Singular systems of differential equations

Pitman Advanced Publishing Program
SAN FRANCISCO · LONDON · MELBOURNE

PITMAN PUBLISHING LIMITED
39 Parker Street, London WC2B 5PB

North American Editorial Office
1020 Plain Street, Marshfield, Massachusetts 02050

North American Sales Office
FEARON PITMAN PUBLISHERS INC.
6 Davis Drive, Belmont, California 94002

Associated Companies
Copp Clark Pitman, Toronto
Pitman Publishing New Zealand Ltd, Wellington
Pitman Publishing Pty Ltd, Melbourne

AMS Subject Classifications: (main) 34A30
(subsidiary) 15A09, 34E15, 93C15

Library of Congress Cataloging in Publication Data

Campbell, Stephen La Vern.
Singular systems of differential equations.

(Research notes in mathematics ; 40)
Includes bibliographical references and index.
1. Differential equations. 2. Equations, Simultaneous. I. Title. II. Series.
QA371.C192 515'.35 79-20908
ISBN 0-8224-8438-2

Manufactured in Great Britain

US ISBN 0-8224-8438-2
UK ISBN 0 273 08438 0

To Gail with love.

Contents

0 Introduction

1. INTRODUCTION

This book is primarily concerned with the differential equation

$$A\dot{\underline{x}} + B\underline{x} = \underline{f} \tag{1}$$

where $\underline{x}$ is a vector function of t, A,B are matrices, and A is, in some sense singular.

There is an extensive literature on what happens if A is a function of t, is invertible in a deleted neighborhood of t_o, and is singular at t_o. An exposition on such "isolated singularities" may be found in [64].

This book is concerned with a different problem. We are not so much interested in when A undergoes a rank change but rather where the rank of A is, in some sense constant, and A is singular for all t. Most of the material in this book has not appeared in text form before. (The primary exception is part of Chapter 3) Some of it appears here for the first time.

Throughout, our first goal is to explicitly solve the equations involved. Sometimes we can only give a procedure which leads to a solution.

In Chapter 1, we introduce some of our notation and review the basic facts we shall need from linear algebra and functional analysis. In particular, the text requires a working knowledge of linear algebra and the functional calculus.

In Chapter 2, we shall develop several particular examples of (1) from Electrical Engineering and Control Theory. As we precede to develop the theory of (1) in the later chapters, these theoretical results will be applied to the examples of Chapter 2.

In Chapter 3, (1) is studied with A,B constant matrices. The solutions of this chapter are algebraic and explicit in nature. They form the basis of several later sections.

Chapter 4 solves (1) with A,B constant by Laplace transforms and applies these results to the impulsive behavior of electrical circuits.

Chapter 5 discusses $A(\varepsilon)\dot{\underline{x}} + B(\varepsilon)\underline{x} = \underline{f}$ where ε is a small positive parameter and A(0) is singular. This falls under the class of problems called "singular perturbation problems." The proofs (but only a few of the results) of this chapter make extensive use of contour integrals that arise in the functional calculus.

Chapter 6 will discuss (1) with A,B functions of t, while Chapter 8 will briefly consider higher order systems. Due to page limitations these chapters are necessarily brief.

In Chapter 7, we consider how one would go about actually solving (1) for an explicitly given A,B,$\underline{f}$.

Theorems, facts, propositions, lemmas, equations and examples are numbered consecutively within each section. A reference to Example 3.2.3 refers to the third example in Section 2 of Chapter 3. If the reader were already in Chapter 3, the reference would be just to Example 2.3. Within Section 2, the reference would be to Example 3.

Exercises are included in the early chapters. The exercises provide a way of presenting material that might be helpful or of interest but which if discussed would break up the continuity of the presentation.

While every attempt has been made to give credit where due, no attempt has been made to make the bibliography complete.

This book is an attempt to present, in an integrated fashion, our approach to a class of problems that we feel are of importance. A complete discussion of alternative approachs has not been attempted though we have tried to allude to and reference them as much as possible.

The author would like to acknowledge the contributions of Nicholas J. Rose and Carl D. Meyer, Jr. They not only participated in much of the research discussed in this book but provided helpful comments on the book itself.

1 Background material

1. INTRODUCTION

The mathematical prerequisites for reading this book are a working knowledge of linear algebra and matrix theory and a familiarity with analysis including complex variables. In Section 2 we present the notation we will use and review some of the concepts in matrix theory. In the remainder of the chapter we treat some of the more specialized topics that will be used in the remainder of the book: Drazin inverses, representations of functions of matrices as contour integrals, and "delta functions." It is hoped that this will keep the need for outside reference books to a minimum.

This book is not about generalized inverses. Rather, they provide a convenient way to express many of our results. The reader interested in a more thorough treatment of generalized inverses is referred to [16].

2. MATRIX THEORY CONCEPTS AND NOTATIONS

The set of complex numbers is denoted by $\mathbb{C}$; the set of real numbers by $\mathbb{R}$. The set of $m \times n$ matrices over $\mathbb{C}$ is denoted by $\mathbb{C}^{m\times n}$; the $m \times n$ matrices over $\mathbb{R}$ by $\mathbb{R}^{m\times n}$. Unless stated otherwise, all matrices will be in $\mathbb{C}^{m\times n}$. The column vectors in the vector space $\mathbb{C}^n \equiv \mathbb{C}^{n\times 1}$ will be denoted by $\underline{u}$, $\underline{x}$ etc.

If $A \in \mathbb{C}^{m\times n}$, we use A^* for the conjugate transpose of A. For vectors $\underline{x},\underline{y} \in \mathbb{C}^n$ we employ the usual inner product $(\underline{x},\underline{y}) = \underline{y}^*\underline{x}$. The norm of a vector $\underline{x} \in \mathbb{C}^n$ is the euclidean norm, $\|\underline{x}\| = (\underline{x},\underline{x})^{\frac{1}{2}}$. For matrices $A \in \mathbb{C}^{n\times n}$, we use the operator norm, $\|A\| = \sup\{\|A\underline{x}\| : \|\underline{x}\| = 1\}$.

If M is a subspace of $\mathbb{C}^n$, dim M denotes the dimension of M. If $A \in \mathbb{C}^{m\times n}$ the range (column space) of A is denoted by $R(A)$ and the null space of A, $\{\underline{x}: A\underline{x} = \underline{0}\}$, by $N(A)$. Recall that $\dim N(A) + \dim R(A) = n$.

Let $M_1,\ldots,M_s$ be subspaces of $\mathbb{C}^n$, the sum of these subspaces is the subspace, $M_1 + \ldots + M_s = \{\underline{z} = \underline{x}_1 + \ldots + \underline{x}_s : \underline{x}_i \in M_i\}$. If $M_i \cap M_j = \{\underline{0}\}$ for $i \neq j$, the subspaces are said to be independent; the sum is then called a direct sum and we write $M_1 \oplus \ldots \oplus M_s$. Recall that $\dim (M_1 \oplus \ldots \oplus M_s) = \dim M_1 + \ldots + \dim M_s$ and if $\underline{x} \in M_1 \oplus \ldots \oplus M_s$, then there exist unique $\underline{x}_i \in M_i$ such that $\underline{x} = \underline{x}_1 + \ldots + \underline{x}_s$.

A projection is a matrix $P \in \mathbb{C}^{n\times n}$ such that $P^2 = P$. It is easily seen that $R(P) + N(P) = \mathbb{C}^n$. Conversely if $\mathbb{C}^n = M \oplus N$, there exists a unique projection P such that $R(P) = M$ and $N(P) = N$; we denote this projection by $P_{M,N}$, the projection onto M along N. If M is a subspace of C^n, the orthogonal complement of M is $M^{\perp} = \{\underline{x} \in \mathbb{C}^n : (\underline{x},\underline{y}) = 0 \text{ for all } \underline{y} \in M\}$. $M^{\perp}$ is a subspace and $M \oplus M^{\perp} = \mathbb{C}^n$. $P_{M,M^{\perp}}$ is denoted by P_M.

If $A \in \mathbb{C}^{m\times n}$, there exists a unique matrix $A^{\dagger} \in C^{n\times m}$ which satisfies the equations $AA^{\dagger}A = A$, $A^{\dagger}AA^{\dagger} = A^{\dagger}$, $AA^{\dagger} = P_{R(A)}$, $A^{\dagger}A = P_{R(A^*)}$. The matrix $A^{\dagger}$ is the Moore-Penrose (generalized) inverse of A. If $A\underline{x} = \underline{b}$ is consistent, then $A^{\dagger}\underline{b}$ is a solution (in fact the solution of minimal norm) and all solutions are given by $\underline{x} = A^{\dagger}\underline{b} + (I - A^{\dagger}A)\underline{h}$ where $\underline{h}$ is arbitrary.

We shall often make use of block matrices. In particular, if $A \in \mathbb{C}^{n\times n}$ is block diagonal, that is A has blocks $A_1,\ldots,A_s$ along the main diagonal and zero blocks elsewhere, we write $A = \text{diag}\,(A_1,\ldots,A_s)$.

The eigenvalues of $A \in \mathbb{C}^{n\times n}$ are the roots of the polynomial $\det(\lambda - A)$. (we often write $\lambda - A$ for $\lambda I - A$ where I is the identity matrix). The spectrum of A is the set of eigenvalues of A and is denoted by $\sigma(A)$. The spectral radius of A is $\rho(A) = \sup\{|\lambda| : \lambda \in \sigma(A)\}$.

If $A,B \in \mathbb{C}^{n\times n}$ we say that A is similar to B in case there exists a nonsingular matrix T such that $A = TBT^{-1}$. Similar matrices represent the same linear transformation or operator on $\mathbb{C}^n$ but with respect to different bases. We shall also make use of the fact that every $A \in \mathbb{C}^{n\times n}$ is similar to a matrix in Jordon Canonical form, that is A is similar to

$$\mathrm{diag}(J_1,\ldots,J_\ell) \text{ where } J_i = \begin{bmatrix} \lambda_i & 1 & \cdots & 0 \\ \vdots & \ddots & \ddots & \vdots \\ \vdots & & \ddots & 1 \\ 0 & \cdots & \cdots & \lambda_i \end{bmatrix}.$$

There may be more than one such block corresponding to the eigenvalue λ_i.

The numerical range of $A \in \mathbb{C}^{n\times n}$ is $W(A) = \{(A\underline{x},\underline{x}) : \|\underline{x}\| = 1\}$ and the numerical radius of A is $w(A) = \sup\{|\lambda| : \lambda \in W(A)\}$. W(A) is a compact convex set which contains $\sigma(A)$. In general W(A) may be larger than the convex hull of $\sigma(A)$. However it is possible to find an invertible matrix T such that $W(TAT^{-1})$ is as close as desired to the convex hull of $\sigma(A)$. To see this we need only consider a typical Jordon block and note that for nonzero $\alpha \in \mathbb{C}$ we have

$$\begin{bmatrix} 1 & & & \\ & \alpha^{-1} & & \\ & & \ddots & \\ & & & \alpha^{-r} \end{bmatrix} \begin{bmatrix} \lambda & 1 & 0 & \cdots & 0 \\ 0 & \lambda & \ddots & & \vdots \\ \vdots & & \ddots & \ddots & 0 \\ \vdots & & & \ddots & 1 \\ 0 & \cdots & \cdots & 0 & \lambda \end{bmatrix} \begin{bmatrix} 1 & & & \\ & \alpha & & \\ & & \alpha^2 & \\ & & & \ddots \ \alpha^r \end{bmatrix} = \begin{bmatrix} \lambda & \alpha & 0 & \cdots & 0 \\ & \ddots & \ddots & & \vdots \\ & & \ddots & \ddots & 0 \\ & & & \ddots & \alpha \\ & & & & \lambda \end{bmatrix}.$$

By taking α sufficiently small our result follows. This observation will be needed in Chapter 5.

A matrix $A \in \mathbb{C}^{n\times n}$ is positive semi-definite if $(A\underline{x},\underline{x}) \geq 0$ for all $\underline{x} \in \mathbb{C}^n$. If A is positive semi-definite, it has a unique positive semi-definite square root which we denote $A^{1/2}$. That is, $(A^{1/2})^2 = A$.

3. THE INDEX AND THE DRAZIN INVERSE

The Drazin inverse can be easily defined using the Jordon canonical form. However, because of the importance of this concept in our work we shall provide a self-contained development that will also serve to review some basic techniques.

If $A \in \mathbb{C}^{n\times n}$, the index of A, written Ind(A), is the least non-negative integer ν such that $N(A^\nu) = N(A^{\nu+1})$ (we adopt the convention that $A^o = I$). Since $N(A^o) = \{\underline{0}\} \subset N(A) \subset N(A^2) \ldots \subset N(A^n) \subset \mathbb{C}^n$ it is clear that $\nu = \text{Ind}(A)$ exists and $0 \le \nu \le n$. If A is nonsingular, Ind(A) = 0, while if A is nilpotent of index ν ($A^\nu = 0$, $A^{\nu-1} \neq 0$), then Ind(A) = ν. The index could also be defined as the least non-negative integer such that $R(A^\nu) = R(A^{\nu+1})$.

Theorem 1.3.1 If $A \in \mathbb{C}^{n\times n}$ and Ind(A) = ν, then $N(A^\nu)$ and $R(A^\nu)$ are invariant subspaces of A and $\mathbb{C}^n = R(A^\nu) \oplus N(A^\nu)$.

The proof of Theorem 1 is left to the reader. Using Theorem 1, we can show that

Theorem 1.3.2 If $A \in \mathbb{C}^{n\times n}$, Ind(A) = ν, dim $R(A^\nu) = s$, dim $N(A)^\nu = t$ $(s + t = n)$, then there exists a nonsingular matrix T such that

$$A = T\begin{bmatrix} C & 0 \\ 0 & N \end{bmatrix}T^{-1} \tag{1}$$

where C is an $s \times s$ nonsingular matrix and N is a $t \times t$ nilpotent matrix with $\nu = \text{Ind}(N)$.

Proof Let $\{\underline{x}_1,\ldots,\underline{x}_s\}$ be a basis for $R(A^\nu)$ and $\{\underline{y}_1,\ldots,\underline{y}_t\}$ be a basis for $N(A^\nu)$. Then $\{\underline{x}_1,\ldots,\underline{x}_s, \underline{y}_1,\ldots,\underline{y}_t\}$ is a basis for $\mathbb{C}^n$. If $\underline{x} \in \mathbb{C}^n$, then there exist unique coordinates α_i, β_i such that $\underline{x} = \Sigma\alpha_i\underline{x}_i + \Sigma\beta_i\underline{y}_i$. Let T be the nonsingular matrix $[\underline{x}_1,\ldots,\underline{x}_s, \underline{y}_1,\ldots,\underline{y}_t]$. Then

$\underline{x} = T\begin{bmatrix}\underline{u}\\ \hline \underline{v}\end{bmatrix}$ where $\underline{u} = \begin{bmatrix}\alpha_1\\ \vdots\\ \alpha_s\end{bmatrix}$, $\underline{v} = \begin{bmatrix}\beta_1\\ \vdots\\ \beta_t\end{bmatrix}$. Note that $\underline{x} \in R(A^\nu)$ if and only if $\underline{v} = \underline{0}$ and $\underline{x} \in N(A^\nu)$ if and only if $\underline{u} = \underline{0}$. If $\underline{y} = A\underline{x}$, we have $\underline{y} = T\begin{bmatrix}\tilde{\underline{u}}\\ \hline \tilde{\underline{v}}\end{bmatrix} = A\underline{x} = AT\begin{bmatrix}\underline{u}\\ \hline \underline{v}\end{bmatrix}$, $\begin{bmatrix}\tilde{\underline{u}}\\ \hline \tilde{\underline{v}}\end{bmatrix} = (T^{-1}AT)\begin{bmatrix}\underline{u}\\ \hline \underline{v}\end{bmatrix} = \begin{bmatrix}C & D\\ E & N\end{bmatrix}\begin{bmatrix}\underline{u}\\ \hline \underline{v}\end{bmatrix}$ where C is $s \times s$ and N is $t \times t$. Thus $\tilde{\underline{u}} = C\underline{u} + D\underline{v}$ and $\tilde{\underline{v}} = E\underline{u} + N\underline{v}$. If $\underline{x} \in R(A^\nu)$, then $\underline{v} = \underline{0}$, and since $\underline{y} = A\underline{x} \in R(A^\nu)$, $\tilde{\underline{v}} = \underline{0}$. Thus $E\underline{u} = \underline{0}$ for all $\underline{u}$ and $E = 0$. Similarly $D = 0$ and $T^{-1}AT = \text{diag}(C,N)$ as claimed.

If $\underline{x} \in N(A^\nu)$, $A^\nu\underline{x} = \underline{0}$ this implies $N^\nu\underline{v} = \underline{0}$ for all $\underline{v}$. Thus $N^\nu = 0$. But then $\text{rank}(A^\nu) = s = \text{rank}(C^\nu)$ and C is $s \times s$. Hence C is invertible. $R(A^{\nu-1}) \neq R(A^\nu)$ now implies that $\text{Ind}(N) = \nu$. □

<u>Definition 1.3.1</u> If $A \in \mathbb{C}^{n\times n}$ is given in the form (1), then the <u>Drazin inverse</u> of A, denoted by A^D, is defined by $A^D = T\begin{bmatrix}C^{-1} & 0\\ 0 & 0\end{bmatrix}T$.

Note that if A is nonsingular, the N block is missing in (1) and $A^D = A^{-1}$ while if A is nilpotent, the C block is missing in (1) and $A^D = 0$. It can be shown that the Drazin inverse is unique.

<u>Theorem 1.3.3</u> If $A \in \mathbb{C}^{n\times n}$ and $\text{Ind}(A) = \nu$, then

$$AA^D = A^DA,\ A^DAA^D = A^D,\ A^{k+1}A^D = A^k \text{ for } k \geq \text{Ind}(A) \tag{2}$$

$$A^k(I - AA^D) = 0,\ k \geq \text{Ind}(A);\ A^k(I - AA^D) \neq 0,\ k < \text{Ind}(A) \tag{3}$$

$$AA^D = P_{R(A^\nu),N(A^\nu)},\ I - AA^D = P_{N(A^\nu),R(A^\nu)} \tag{4}$$

The proof of Theorem 3 follows directly from the definition of A^D. The properties (2) completely characterize A^D and are often used as the definition of A^D.

We note also that $N(A^\nu) = N(A^D)$ and $R(A^\nu) = R(A^D)$. In addition $\underline{x} \in N(A^\nu)$ if and only if $AA^D\underline{x} = \underline{0}$ which holds if and only if $\underline{x} = (I - AA^D)\underline{x}$.

In case Ind(A) = 0 or 1 (the N block in (1), if present, is 0), the Drazin inverse of A is often called the <u>group inverse</u> and denoted by $A^{\#}$. The group inverse has the additional property that $AA^{\#}A = A$. From Definition 1 we also have;

<u>Theorem 1.3.4</u> If $A \in \mathbb{C}^{n\times n}$ and 0 is an eigenvalue of A of multiplicity t, then 0 is an eigenvalue of A^D of multiplicity t. If $\lambda \neq 0$ is an eigenvalue of A of multiplicity m, then λ^{-1} is an eigenvalue of A^D of multiplicity m.

<u>Theorem 1.3.5</u> If $A \in \mathbb{C}^{n\times n}$, A^D is a polynomial in A of degree n - 1 or less.

<u>Proof</u> In (1), C is a nonsingular $s \times s$ matrix and N a nilpotent $t \times t$ matrix where $s + t = n$. By the Cayley-Hamilton theorem $C^{-t-1} = p(C)$ where p is a polynomial of degree s - 1 or less. By direct calculation we find $A^t p(A) = A^D$ since $t \geq \nu = \text{Ind}(A)$. □

4. <u>FUNCTIONS OF A MATRIX</u>

Throughout this section we use the following notation: for $A \in \mathbb{C}^{n\times n}$ let its characteristic polynomial be $c(\lambda) = (\lambda - \lambda_1)^{m_1}(\lambda - \lambda_2)^{m_2} \ldots (\lambda - \lambda_s)^{m_s}$ where the eigenvalues λ_i are distinct and $m_1 + m_2 + \ldots + m_s = n$. Let $\nu_i = \text{Ind}(\lambda_i - A)$ and $N_i = N((\lambda_i - A)^{\nu_i})$. We know that N_i is an invariant subspace for A and $\dim N_i = m_i$. We also know that $E_i = I - (\lambda_i - A)(\lambda_i - A)^D$

is a projection on N_i. Since E_i and E_j are polynomials in A we have $E_iE_j = E_jE_i$. Other properties of N_i and E_i are;

<u>Theorem 1.4.1</u> Using the notation above: (a) $N_i \cap N_j = \{\underline{0}\}$, $i \neq j$, (b) $E_iE_j = E_jE_i = 0$, $i \neq j$ (c) $\mathbb{C}^n = N_1 \oplus N_2 \oplus \ldots \oplus N_s$ (d) $I = E_1 + E_2 + \ldots E_s$.

Theorem 1 may be proved directly or by inductively applying the proof of Theorem 3.2 to $A - \lambda_i$ for $i = 1,\ldots,s$.

<u>Theorem 1.4.2</u> If $p(\lambda)$ is a polynomial of degree N, then

$$p(A) = \sum_{i=1}^{s} \sum_{k=0}^{\nu_i - 1} \frac{p^{(k)}(\lambda_i)}{k!} (A - \lambda_i)^k E_i \tag{1}$$

<u>Proof</u> By Taylor's theorem, $p(\lambda) = \sum_{k=0}^{N} p^{(k)}(\lambda_i)(\lambda - \lambda_i)^k/k!$, thus $p(A) = \sum_{k=0}^{N} p^{(k)}(\lambda_i)(A - \lambda_i)^k/k!$. But $p(A)E_i = \sum_{k=0}^{\nu_i - 1} p^{(k)}(\lambda_i)(A - \lambda_i)E_i/k!$ since $(A - \lambda_i)^k E_i = 0$ for $k \geq \nu_i$. The result now follows since $p(A) = p(A)(E_1 + \ldots + E_s)$. □

<u>Theorem 1.4.3</u> If f is an analytic function of $\lambda \in C$ for $|\lambda| < R$ and $\rho(A) < R$, then f(A) exists and

$$f(A) = \sum_{i=1}^{s} \sum_{k=0}^{\nu_i - 1} \frac{f^{(k)}(\lambda_i)}{k!} (A - \lambda_i)^k E_i \tag{2}$$

<u>Proof</u> If $f(\lambda) = \sum_0^{\infty} a_n \lambda^n$, $|\lambda| < R$, let $S_N(\lambda) = \sum_0^N a_n \lambda_n$. By Theorem 2 we have $S_N(A) = \sum_{i=1}^{s} \sum_{k=0}^{\nu_i - 1} \frac{S_N^{(k)}(\lambda_i)}{k!} (A - \lambda_i)^k E_i$. Since the sum is a finite sum and $S_N^{(k)}(\lambda_i) \to f^{(k)}(\lambda_i)$ as $N \to \infty$, we may let $N \to \infty$ to obtain the result. □

Note that, since $\nu_i \leq m_i$ and $(A - \lambda_i)^k E_i = 0$, $k \geq \nu_i$, we may replace ν_i by m_i in (2). Thus only the algebraic multiplicities of the eigenvalues are needed to find $f(A)$. A useful consequence of (2) is that

Theorem 1.4.4 If f, g are analytic for $|\lambda| < R$ and $\rho(A) < R$, then $f(A) = g(A)$ if and only if $f^{(k)}(\lambda_i) = g^{(k)}(\lambda_i)$ for $k = 0,1,\ldots,\nu_{i-1}$ and $i = 1,\ldots,s$. In particular, if $r(\lambda)$ is a polynomial such that $f^{(k)}(\lambda_i) = r^{(k)}(\lambda_i)$ for $k = 0,1,\ldots,m_{i-1}$ and $i = 1,\ldots,s$, then $f(A) = r(A)$.

Thus to find $f(A)$ it is only necessary to find the Hermite interpolating polynomial described in Theorem 4.

The most important matrix function for our purpose is the matrix exponential. Since $e^{\lambda} = \Sigma\lambda^n/n!$ converges for all λ, e^A exists for every square matrix and $e^A = \sum_{i=1}^{s}\sum_{k=0}^{\nu_i-1} \frac{e^{\lambda_i}}{k}(A - \lambda_i)^k E_i$. Since $e^{\lambda}e^{-\lambda} = 1$, we have by Theorem 4 that $e^A e^{-A} = I$. Thus e^A is invertible and $(e^A)^{-1} = e^{-A}$. For $t \in \mathbb{R}$ we find that

$$e^{At} = \sum_{i=1}^{s}\sum_{k=0}^{\nu_i-1} \frac{t^k e^{\lambda_i t}}{k!}(A - \lambda_i)^k E_i. \tag{3}$$

since $(At - \lambda_i t)^k(I - (\lambda_i t - At)(\lambda_i t - At)^D) = t^k(A - \lambda_i)^k E_i$ and the eigenvalues of At are $t\lambda_i$. We may also prove from (3) that $\frac{d}{dt}e^{At} = Ae^{At} = e^{At}A$. Thus $e^{At}\underline{x}_0$ provides a solution to $\dot{\underline{x}} = A\underline{x}$, $\underline{x}(0) = \underline{x}_0$.

Example 1.4.1 Find e^{At} if $A = \begin{bmatrix} 3 & -1 & 1 \\ 2 & 0 & 1 \\ 1 & -1 & 2 \end{bmatrix}$. We find $\sigma(A) = \{1,2,3\}$, thus $e^{At} = r(A)$ where $r(\lambda) = \alpha + \beta\lambda + \gamma\lambda^2$ is determined from the equations $e^t = \alpha + \beta + \gamma$, $e^{2t} = \alpha + 2\beta + 4\gamma$, $te^{2t} = \beta + 4\gamma$. Solving these equations we obtain $\alpha = 2te^{2t} - 3e^{2t} + 4e^{t}$, $\beta = -3te^{2t} + 4e^{2t} - 4e^{t}$, $\gamma = te^{2t} - e^{2t} + e^{t}$. Thus we obtain

$$e^{At} = \alpha I + \beta A + \gamma A^2 = \begin{bmatrix} e^{2t}+te^{2t} & -te^{2t} & te^{2t} \\ -e^{t}+e^{2t}+te^{2t} & e^{t}-te^{2t} & te^{2t} \\ -e^{t}+e^{2t} & e^{t}-e^{2t} & e^{2t} \end{bmatrix}.$$

Alternatively we have for any analytic function f, $f(A) = f(1)E_1 + f(2)E_2 + f'(2)(A - 2)E_2$. Setting $f(\lambda) = (\lambda - 2)^2$ we find $(A - 2)^2 = E_1$ and since $E_1 + E_2 = I$, $E_2 = I - (A - 2)^2$. Thus

$$f(A) = f(1)\begin{bmatrix} 0 & 0 & 0 \\ -1 & 1 & 0 \\ -1 & 1 & 0 \end{bmatrix} + f(2)\begin{bmatrix} 1 & 0 & 0 \\ 1 & 0 & 0 \\ 1 & -1 & 1 \end{bmatrix} + f'(2)\begin{bmatrix} 1 & -1 & 1 \\ 1 & -1 & 1 \\ 0 & 0 & 0 \end{bmatrix}.$$

Setting $f(\lambda) = e^{\lambda t}$ we reproduce the result above. This method has the advantage that once the projections E_i are determined for a particular matrix A, they may be used to evaluate any admissible function of A.

The Drazin inverse also has a spectral representation and can be computed in the same manner as for analytic functions.

<u>Theorem 1.4.5</u> Let $A \in \mathbb{C}^{n\times n}$ be singular with characteristic polynomial $c(\lambda) = \lambda^{m_1}(\lambda - \lambda_2)^{m_2}\ldots(\lambda - \lambda_s)^{m_s}$ where $\lambda_i \neq 0$ and $m_1 + m_2 + \ldots + m_s = n$. Then $A^D = r(A)$ where $r(\lambda) = \lambda^{m_1}(a_0 + a_1\lambda + \ldots + a_{n-m_i-1}\lambda^{n-m_i-1})$ and $r(\lambda)$ may be computed from the equations

$$r^{(k)}(\lambda_i) = \frac{(-1)^k k!}{\lambda_i^{k+1}}, \quad k = 0,1,\ldots,m_{i-1}; \; i = 2,\ldots,s. \tag{4}$$

Also

$$A^D = \sum_{i=2}^{s} \sum_{k=0}^{m_i-1} \frac{(-1)^k}{\lambda_i^{k+1}} (A - \lambda_i)^k E_i. \tag{5}$$

Proof We know that $A^D = r(A)$, a polynomial in A, which has the form given. Since $A^{m_1+1}A^D = A^{m_1}$ we have $A^{m_1+1}r(A) = A^{m_1}$. Let $f(\lambda) = \lambda^{m_1+1}r(\lambda)$ and $g(\lambda) = \lambda^{m_1}$. Then, $f^{(k)}(\lambda_i) = g^{(k)}(\lambda_i)$ by Theorem 4 since $f(A) = g(A)$. Computing these derivatives yields (4). Equation (5) follows immediately from (4). □

Example 1.4.2 If $A \in \mathbb{C}^{4\times 4}$ has $\sigma(A) = \{0,0,1,1\}$ we have $A^D = r(A)$ where $r(\lambda) = \lambda^2(a_0 + a_1\lambda)$. Equation (4) yields $1 = a_0 + a_1$, $-1 = 2a_0 + 3a_1$ where $a_0 = 4$ and $a_1 = -3$. Thus $A^D = A^2(4I - 3A)$.

5. REPRESENTATION OF MATRIX FUNCTIONS BY CONTOUR INTEGRALS

In some of the later chapters it will be very helpful to use representations of matrix functions by contour integrals. Recall that if $f(z)$ is analytic in and on a simple closed rectifiable curve or contour, C, then $\int_C f(z)dz = 0$. Also if z is in the interior of C, then

$$f(z) = \frac{1}{2\pi i}\int_C \frac{f(\lambda)}{\lambda - z}d\lambda \text{ and } f^{(k)}(z) = \frac{k!}{2\pi i}\int_C \frac{f(\lambda)}{(\lambda - z)^{k+1}}d\lambda \tag{1}$$

We obtain similar representations for functions of a matrix. If $A \in \mathbb{C}^{n\times n}$, the matrix function $(\lambda - A)^{-1}$ is called the resolvent of A. It is analytic for $\lambda \notin \sigma(A)$. If the characteristic polynomial of A is $c(\lambda) = (\lambda - \lambda_1)^{m_1}\ldots(\lambda - \lambda_s)^{m_s}$ where the λ_i are distinct and $m_1 + \ldots + m_s = n$, then the spectral representation of the resolvent is

$$(\lambda - A)^{-1} = \sum_{i=1}^{s}\sum_{k=0}^{m_i-1} \frac{(A - \lambda_i)^k}{(\lambda - \lambda_i)^{k+1}}E_i \quad , \quad \lambda \notin \sigma(A) \tag{2}$$

where $E_i = I - (\lambda_i - A)(\lambda_i - A)^D$ is a projection.

Theorem 1.5.1 If $A \in \mathbb{C}^{n\times n}$ and f is analytic for $|\lambda| < R$ and $\rho(A) < R$, then $f(A) = \frac{1}{2\pi i}\int_C f(\lambda)(\lambda - A)^{-1}d\lambda$ where C is a contour lying in the disc $|\lambda| < R$ and enclosing all the eigenvalues of A.

Proof Using (2) we have

$$\frac{1}{2\pi i}\int_C f(\lambda)(\lambda - A)^{-1}d\lambda = \sum_{i=1}^{s}\sum_{k=0}^{m_i-1} \frac{1}{2\pi i}\int_C \frac{f(\lambda)}{(\lambda - \lambda_i)^{k+1}}\, d\lambda (A - \lambda_i)^k E_i$$

$$= \sum_{i=1}^{s}\sum_{k=0}^{m_i-1} \frac{f^{(k)}(\lambda_i)}{k!}(A - \lambda_i)^k E_i = f(A). \square$$

Corollary 1.5.1 If $\sigma(A) = \sigma_1 \cup \sigma_2$ where σ_1, σ_2 are disjoint sets of eigenvalues and C_1 is a contour containing σ_1 in its interior and σ_2 in its exterior, then

$$\frac{1}{2\pi i}\int_{C_1} f(\lambda)(\lambda - A)^{-1}d\lambda = f(A)P = f(AP)P \quad \text{where } P \text{ is the projection}$$

$$P = \sum_{\lambda\in\sigma_1} (I - (\lambda - A)(\lambda - A)^D) = \frac{1}{2\pi i}\int_{C_1} (\lambda - A)^{-1}d\lambda.$$

If C_t is a continuously parameterized family of contours for t in some interval I and $C_t \cap \sigma(A) = \emptyset$ for all t and if f is analytic on and inside all the C_t, then $\frac{1}{2\pi i}\int_{C_t} f(\lambda)(\lambda - A)^{-1}d\lambda$ is independent of t. This observation will be useful later.

6. DELTA FUNCTIONS

Occasionally we shall talk about the impulsive behavior of systems. A convenient way to do so is with delta functions. Delta functions will also provide a way to give the appropriate kernels in the section on boundary values.

The delta function $\delta(t)$ and its $i^{\underline{th}}$ derivative, $\delta^{(i)}(t)$, are not actually functions, but rather objects in a larger space to which the operations of differentiation, integration, and taking Laplace transforms may be extended. It is not our intention to carefully define delta functions but rather just state the properties they have.

$\delta(t)$ has the following properties. For $t \neq 0$, it is a "function" and is identically zero. $\delta(0)$ is undefined. However,

$$\int_a^b f(t)\delta(t)dt = f(0) \tag{1}$$

for any function f that is continuous at zero and interval [a,b] with $0 \in [a,b]$.

In particular, $\int_a^b \delta(t)dt = 1$ and

$$\int_{-1}^t \delta(s)ds = h(t) = \begin{cases} 0 \text{ if } t < 0 \\ 1 \text{ if } t \geq 0 \end{cases} . \tag{2}$$

Thus $\delta(t)$ can be viewed as the derivative of the h(t) in (2).

The Laplace transform of δ is $L[\delta] = \int_0^\infty e^{-st}\delta(t)dt = 1$. For integers $i \geq 1$, $\delta^{(i)}(t)$ is the $i^{\underline{th}}$ derivative of $\delta(t)$. It is also a function for $t \neq 0$ that is identically zero. In addition if f(t) is i-times continuously differentiable at 0, and $0 \in [a,b]$, then

$$\int_a^b f(t)\delta^{(i)}(t)dt = (-1)^i f^{(i)}(0). \tag{3}$$

Similarly, $L[\delta^{(i)}] = \int_0^\infty e^{-st}\delta^{(i)}(t)dt = s^i$.

The delta functions behave in formulas much like functions. In particular, integration by parts holds with the proper interpretation. Also if c is a real number, f is i-times differentiable at c, and $c \in [a,b]$, then

$$\int_a^b f(t)\delta^{(i)}(t - c)dt = (-1)^i f^{(i)}(c).$$

Intuitively, one thinks of $\delta(t - c)$ as a "sudden impulse" at time c. It can be shown that, in the appropriate sense, $\delta(t)$ is actually the limit of functions f_n such that $\int_{-\infty}^{\infty} f_n(t)dt = 1$, $f_n(t) = 0$ if $|t| > 1/n$. For example, we could take $f_n(t) = 0$ if $t \notin [0,1/n]$ and $f_n(t) = n$ for $0 \leq t \leq 1/n$. For n large, these f_n look very much like what one would envision a "sudden impulse" to be.

7. EXERCISES

1. If $A \in \mathbb{C}^{n\times n}$ and $0 \neq \alpha \in \mathbb{C}$, show that $(\alpha A)^D = \alpha^{-1}A^D$.
2. If $A \in \mathbb{C}^{n\times n}$ and $A = T\{\text{diag}(A_1,A_2)\}T^{-1}$ where A_1, A_2 are square, show that $A^D = T\{\text{diag}(A_1^D,A_2^D)\}T^{-1}$.
3. If $A \in \mathbb{C}^{n\times n}$ and C is square show that $A^D = \begin{bmatrix} 0 & 0 \\ B & C \end{bmatrix}^D = \begin{bmatrix} 0 & 0 \\ (C^D)^2 B & C^D \end{bmatrix}$.
4. In problem 3 show that A has index 1 if and only if C has index 0 or 1 and $C^D CB = B$.
5. If $M \in \mathbb{C}^{n\times n}$ and A, C are square, show that $M^D = \begin{bmatrix} A & B \\ 0 & C \end{bmatrix}^D = \begin{bmatrix} A^D & X \\ 0 & C^D \end{bmatrix}$ where

   $$X = (A^D)^2 \sum_{i=0}^{\ell-1} \{(A^D)^i BC^i\}(I - CC^D) + (I - AA^D) \sum_{i=0}^{k-1} \{A^i B(C^D)^i\}(C^D)^2 - A^D BC^D$$

   with $k = \text{Ind}(A)$ and $\ell = \text{Ind}(C)$. (For a proof see [16, p. 139])
6. Show that if $AB = BA$, then $(AB)^D = B^D A^D = A^D B^D$.
7. Let $c(\lambda)$ be the characteristic polynomial of A show

   (a) if $c(\lambda) = \lambda^2(\lambda^2 + 5\lambda + 1)$, $A^D = -24A^3 - 115$

(b) if $c(\lambda) = \lambda^2(\lambda^4 + \lambda^3 + \lambda^2 + \lambda + 1)$, $A^D = A^4$

(c) $c(\lambda) = \lambda^4(\lambda - 1)^3$, $A^D = A^4(1 - 5(A - 1) + 15(A - 1)^2)$.

8. If A is hermitian, i.e. $A = A^*$, show that $\mathrm{Ind}(A) \leq 1$.

9. If $A \in \mathbb{C}^{n\times n}$, show that $A^D = \frac{1}{2\pi i}\int_C \lambda^{-1}(\lambda - A)^{-1}d\lambda$ where C encloses all the eigenvalues of A except the zero eigenvalue.

2 Examples of singular problems

1. INTRODUCTION

As mentioned in Chapter 0, this book is concerned with systems of the form

$$A\dot{\underline{x}} + B\underline{x} = \underline{f} \tag{1}$$

and its discrete analog

$$A\underline{x}_{k+1} + B\underline{x}_k = \underline{f}_k, \tag{2}$$

where A is singular. While we are primarily interested in the mathematical aspects of (1), it is helpful to know where such systems occur. For one thing, it helps justify the study of (1). Secondly, it is interesting to consider the 'physical' interpretation of some of our assumptions and results. Of course, one can talk of "systems theory" applications of (1), but that, in a sense, is the same as the original mathematical theory. Instead, we have preferred to present several problems, some specific, some general. Our review will be brief, but hopefully sufficient to show where (1) can occur.

2. CONTROL PROBLEMS

There are two basic types of control problems we shall be concerned with, optimal and constrained.

In general, an optimal control problem involves a process $\underline{x}$, which is regulated by a control $\underline{u}$. The problem is to choose a control $\underline{u}$ so as to cause $\underline{x}$ to have some type of desired behavior and minimize a cost $J[\underline{x},\underline{u}]$. The cost may, of course, take many forms. It may be time, total energy, or something else. The desired behavior of the process may range from going to zero to hitting a moving "target." Finally, the process may depend on the control in a variety of ways, often nonlinear. We shall be interested in the following problems.

Let A,B be $n \times n$ and $n \times m$ matrices respectively. All matrices and scalars are allowed to be complex though, of course, in many applications they are real. Let Q,H be positive semi-definite $m \times m$ and $n \times n$ matrices. Finally, let $\underline{x},\underline{u}$ denote vector valued functions of the real variable t. $\underline{x}$ is $n \times 1$ while $\underline{u}$ is $m \times 1$.

We consider the autonomous (time independent coefficients) control process

$$\dot{\underline{x}} = A\underline{x} + B\underline{u} \tag{1}$$

on the time interval $[t_o,t_1]$ with quadratic cost functional

$$J[\underline{x},\underline{u}] = \frac{1}{2}\int_{t_o}^{t_1} (H\underline{x},\underline{x}) + (Q\underline{u},\underline{u})dt. \tag{2}$$

If one has a fixed pair of vectors $\underline{x}_o,\underline{x}_1$ such that there exists controls $\underline{u}$ so that the process $\underline{x}$ is at $\underline{x}_o$ at time t_o and $\underline{x}_1$ at time t_1, then one can ask for a control that minimizes the cost (2) subject to the restraint that $\underline{x}(t_o) = \underline{x}_o$, $\underline{x}(t_1) = \underline{x}_1$.

Using the theory of Lagrange multipliers one gets the system of equations

$$\begin{aligned} &\dot{\underline{\lambda}} + A^*\underline{\lambda} + H\underline{x} = \underline{0} \\ &\dot{\underline{x}} - A\underline{x} - B\underline{u} = \underline{0} \\ &B^*\underline{\lambda} + Q\underline{u} = \underline{0} \end{aligned} \tag{3}$$

as necessary conditions for optimization.

If Q is invertible, then $\underline{u}$ can be eliminated from the second equation and the resulting system formed by the first two equations solved directly. We shall be most interested then in the case when Q is not invertible, though our results will include the case when Q is invertible.

The system (3) can be rewritten as

$$\begin{bmatrix} I & 0 & 0 \\ 0 & I & 0 \\ 0 & 0 & 0 \end{bmatrix} \begin{bmatrix} \dot{\underline{\lambda}} \\ \dot{\underline{x}} \\ \dot{\underline{u}} \end{bmatrix} + \begin{bmatrix} A^* & H & 0 \\ 0 & -A & -B \\ B^* & 0 & Q \end{bmatrix} \begin{bmatrix} \underline{\lambda} \\ \underline{x} \\ \underline{u} \end{bmatrix} = \begin{bmatrix} \underline{0} \\ \underline{0} \\ \underline{0} \end{bmatrix} . \qquad (4)$$

Note that (4) has leading coefficient singular and is of the form (1.1). This problem (1), (2) will be referred to as the Basic Quadratic Cost Problem.

Optimal control problems with singular matrices in the quadratic cost functional have received much attention. They occur naturally as a first order approximation to more general optimal control problems. [36] surveys the known results on one such problem with singular matrices in the cost. See also [1].

Many variations on (1) - (2) are possible.

For example, suppose that the cost is given by $\int_{t_o}^{t_1} (H\underline{x},\underline{x}) + (Q\underline{u},\underline{u}) + (\underline{x},\underline{a})dt$ where $\underline{a}$ is a vector. Then the right hand side of (4) has $\underline{\alpha} = [\underline{a}^*,\underline{0}^*,\underline{0}^*]^*$ instead of the zero vector.

Another variation on the same type of problem is process (1) with the cost functional $J[\underline{x},\underline{u}] = \frac{1}{2}\int_{t_o}^{t_1} (H\underline{x},\underline{x}) + 2(\underline{u},C\underline{x}) + (Q\underline{u},u)dt$ where $\begin{bmatrix} H & C \\ C^* & Q \end{bmatrix}$ is positive semi-definite, [1]. In this case the system to be solved is

$$\begin{bmatrix} I & 0 & 0 \\ 0 & I & 0 \\ 0 & 0 & 0 \end{bmatrix} \begin{bmatrix} \dot{\underline{\lambda}} \\ \dot{\underline{x}} \\ \dot{\underline{u}} \end{bmatrix} + \begin{bmatrix} A^* & H & C^* \\ 0 & -A & -B \\ B^* & C & Q \end{bmatrix} \begin{bmatrix} \underline{\lambda} \\ \underline{x} \\ \underline{u} \end{bmatrix} = \begin{bmatrix} \underline{0} \\ \underline{0} \\ \underline{0} \end{bmatrix} . \qquad (5)$$

Note that (5) is in the form of (1.1).

A different type of control problem is one where the output is specified. Given output $\underline{y}$, state vector $\underline{x}$, and process $\dot{\underline{x}} = A\underline{x} + B\underline{u}$, find a control $\underline{u}$ such that $\underline{y} = C\underline{x} + D\underline{u}$. The appropriate system then is

$$\begin{bmatrix} I & 0 \\ 0 & 0 \end{bmatrix} \begin{bmatrix} \dot{\underline{x}} \\ \dot{\underline{u}} \end{bmatrix} + \begin{bmatrix} -A & -B \\ C & D \end{bmatrix} \begin{bmatrix} \underline{x} \\ \underline{u} \end{bmatrix} = \begin{bmatrix} \underline{0} \\ \underline{y} \end{bmatrix} . \qquad (6)$$

If $\underline{y}$ and $\underline{u}$ are the same size vectors, then (6) is the nonhomogeneous form of equation (1.1).

One frequently does not want to have D a square matrix in (6). In this case the block matrices in (6) are rectangular.

Another problem, closely related to the preceding, for which our results have proved helpful is the General Continuous Linear Programming Problem [59]. This problem is a continuous version of the linear programming problem.

Let $K(t,s)$, $B(t)$ be $m \times n$ matrices, $\underline{x}(t)$ an n-vector, $\underline{b}(t)$ an m-vector, $[0,T]$ a fixed time period. Finally, let $\underline{x} \geq \underline{0}$ mean that each entry of $\underline{x}(t)$ is non-negative. Then the general continuous linear programming problem is to minimize

$$\int_0^T \underline{c}^*(t)\underline{x}(t)dt \qquad (7)$$

subject to

$$B(t)\underline{x}(t) + \int_0^t K(t,s)\underline{x}(s)ds = \underline{b}(t), \ \underline{x} \geq \underline{0}, \ t \in [0,T]. \qquad (8)$$

An important special case of this is the following linear optimal control problem; minimize

$$\int_0^T \underline{c}_1^*(t)\underline{x}(t) + \underline{c}_2^*(t)\underline{u}(t)dt \tag{9}$$

subject to

$$\begin{aligned} \dot{\underline{x}} &= A\underline{x} + B\underline{u} + \underline{b}_1 \\ \underline{0} &= C\underline{x} + D\underline{u} + \underline{b}_2 \\ \underline{x} &\geq \underline{0},\ \underline{u} \geq \underline{0},\ \underline{x}(0) \text{ given, } t \in [0,T]. \end{aligned} \tag{10}$$

Note that (8) is an integrated form of (10) and that $\underline{x}$ in (7) is $\begin{bmatrix} \underline{x} \\ \underline{u} \end{bmatrix}$ in (9) - (10). In [59], Perold develops a theory for (7) - (8) and (9) - (10) which parallels closely that of the ordinary simplex method. This necessitates characterizing basic feasible solutions and extreme points of (10). The results of Chapter 3 play a basic role in this development.

These control problems all have their discrete analogues. Discrete control systems arise both as discretized versions of continuous systems and as systems of independent interest. For example, a discrete analogue of (1) - (2) is:

Discrete control problem. Let A, B, Q, H be matrices of sizes $n \times n$, $n \times m$, $m \times m$, and $n \times n$ respectively. Assume that Q, H are positive semi-definite. Let N be a fixed integer. Given the process

$$\underline{x}_{i+1} = A\underline{x}_i + B\underline{u}_i, \quad i = 0,\ldots,N-1, \tag{11}$$

the cost

$$J[\underline{x},\underline{u}] = \frac{1}{2}\sum_{i=0}^{N} (H\underline{x}_i,\underline{x}_i) + (Q\underline{u}_i,\underline{u}_i), \tag{12}$$

and the initial position $\underline{x}_o$, find the control sequence which minimizes the cost. Here $\underline{x} = \{\underline{x}_i\}$, $\underline{u} = \{\underline{u}_i\}$.

The discrete version of (6) would be

$$\begin{aligned} \underline{x}_{i+1} &= A\underline{x}_i + B\underline{u}_i \\ \underline{y}_i &= C\underline{x}_i + D\underline{u}_i . \end{aligned} \tag{13}$$

More specific examples of discrete systems are given in Sections 4 and 5 of this chapter.

3. ELECTRICAL CIRCUITS AND IMPULSIVE BEHAVIOR

The ideas of this section could be applied to mechanical and other systems of a non-electrical nature but for purposes of introduction it is convenient to think in terms of electrical circuits. We shall be concerned with circuits whose only elements are inductors, capacitors, and resistors. If q is charge and i = dq/dt is the current, then the voltage drop across a circuit element is proportional to q for capacitors, i = dq/dt for resistors, and $di/dt = d^2q/dt^2$ for inductors. Applying Kirchoff's laws to the currents in the different loops, we get a model for the circuit which is a system of differential equations;

$$A\dot{\underline{x}} + B\underline{x} = \underline{f} \tag{1}$$

If both d^2q/dt and q are present, then the original second order system is written in the form of (1) by the usual, $\underline{x} = \begin{bmatrix} \underline{x}_1 \\ \underline{x}_2 \end{bmatrix}$, $\underline{x}_1 = \underline{q}$, $\underline{x}_2 = d\underline{q}/dt$, change of variables.

If some of the terms in A are small, then it is of interest to analyze (1) when these small terms are set equal to zero. This may make A singular. Such singular perturbation problems are discussed in Section 6.

Another possibility is that the vector $\underline{x}$ has many components and there is an unknown redundancy in (1) which causes A to be singular.

However, of more importance is the following problem. Suppose that the circuit is operating at time $t < 0$. At time $t = 0$, the circuit is reassembled in a different fashion in such a manner that the value at $t = 0$, (denoted $\underline{x}(0^-) = \lim_{t \to 0^-} \underline{x}(t)$) is inconsistent with the new system. The result is an impulsive behavior of the system to a new state which is consistent with the new equations. An intuitive example is the "sparking" which sometimes occurs when subsystems are suddenly connected together.

This reassmebly could be due to component failure or the throwing of a switch. The same ideas are also of importance in examining how the properties of interconnected subsystems are reflected in the composite system. For an extensive analysis and discussion of these problems see [63] which is written in systems theory language.

For a very simple example of an impulsive behavior consider a circuit consisting of a capacitor of capacitance C and a voltage source of constant voltage E forming a simple circuit for $t < 0$. Then $q(t) = CE$, $i(t) = 0$ for $t < 0$. At time $t = 0$, the capacitor is shorted out so that for $t > 0$, $q(t) = 0$, $i(t) = 0$. In this case, q has a jump discontinuity at $t = 0$, and $i(t) = -CE\delta(t)$ exhibits an impulse at $t = 0$.

4. THE LESLIE POPULATION GROWTH MODEL AND BACKWARD POPULATION PROJECTION

Suppose that a population is partitioned according to age groups. Given specific rates of fertility and mortality, along with an initial age distribution, the Leslie model provides the age distribution of the survivors and descendants of the initial population at successive, discrete points in time.

It is a standard demographic practice to consider only one sex at a time. We will consider only the female portion of a population. Select a unit of time (e.g. 5 years, or 1 year, or 10 seconds, or .5 microseconds, etc.). Let Δt denote one unit of time. Select an integer m such that $m(\Delta t)$ is the maximum age to be considered. Construct m disjoint age classes or age intervals; $A_i = (i\Delta t, (i + 1)\Delta t]$ for $0 \leq i \leq m - 1$. Let t_o denote an initial point in time and for each integer n let $t_n = n(\Delta t) + t_o$. Let us agree to say a <u>female belongs</u> to A_k at time t if she is living at time t, and her age lies in A_k at time t. To define the survival and birth rates, let $p_k(t)$ be the probability that a female in A_k at time t will be in A_{k+1} at time $t + \Delta t$ (survival rates). Let $b_k(t)$ be the expected number of daughters produced in the time interval $[t, t + \Delta t)$, which are alive at time $t + \Delta t$, by a female in A_k (birth rates). Furthermore, let $n_k(t)$ be the expected number of females in A_k at time t. Finally, let $\underline{n}(t) = [n_1(t), \ldots, n_m(t)]^*$. For convenience, adopt the notation $\underline{n}(t_i) = \underline{n}(i)$, $p_k(t_i) = p_k(i)$, and $b_k(t_i) = b_k(i)$. Suppose we know the age distribution of our population at time t_i, $\underline{n}(i)$. From this together with the survival rates and birth rates, we can obtain the expected age distribution of the population at time t_{i+1} as

$$\begin{bmatrix} n_1(i+1) \\ n_2(i+1) \\ \vdots \\ n_m(i+1) \end{bmatrix} = \begin{bmatrix} b_1(i) & b_2(i) & \cdots & b_{m-1}(i) & b_m(i) \\ p_1(i) & 0 & \cdots & 0 & 0 \\ 0 & \ddots & \ddots & \vdots & \vdots \\ \vdots & & \ddots & \ddots & \vdots \\ 0 & \cdots & \cdots & p_{m-1}(i) & 0 \end{bmatrix} \begin{bmatrix} n_1(i) \\ n_2(i) \\ \vdots \\ n_m(i) \end{bmatrix} \quad (1)$$

or $\underline{n}(i + 1) = T(i)\underline{n}(i)$. The expression (1) is the <u>Leslie model</u>. Many times, the survival rates and birth rates are constant with respect to the time scale under consideration. Let us make this assumption and write

$p_k(t) = p_k$, $b_k(t) = b_k$, so that (1) becomes $\underline{n}(i + 1) = T\underline{n}(i)$. We shall refer to T as the Leslie matrix. Given an initial population distribution, $\underline{n}(0)$, it is easy to project forward into time and produce the expected population at a future time, say $t = t_k$, since $\underline{n}_k = T^k\underline{n}(0)$.

We wish to deal with the problem of projecting a population distribution backward in time in order to determine what kind of population distribution there had to exist in the past, in order to produce the present population distribution. Such a problem might arise, for example, in a situation where one has statistics giving the age distribution for population A at only the time t_i and other statistics giving the age distribution for population B at a different time, say t_{i+x}. If one wishes to make a comparison of the two populations at time t_i, then it is necessary to project population B backward in time.

The problem of backward population projection is trivial when T is nonsingular. If T is singular, the problem is more interesting. The Leslie matrix is very often singular since not all age groups have offspring.

Frequently, members of a population are added to or removed from a population by factors other than birth or death. For example, immigration of people, harvesting or stocking of animal populations. In these cases, the model is

$$\underline{n}(i + 1) = T\underline{n}(i) + \underline{f}(i + 1). \tag{2}$$

If we wish to perform backward projection from time ℓ we get, setting $k = \ell - 1$,

$$T\underline{n}(k + 1) - \underline{n}(k) = -\underline{f}(k) \quad , \quad k = 0,1,\ldots \tag{3}$$

which is in the form (1.2).

Note that if (3) is viewed as a process and $\underline{f}(k)$ as a control, this could become a control problem. That is, to achieve a desired state $\underline{n}(i)$, from an initial state $\underline{n}(0)$ what should the $\underline{f}(j)$ be for $0 \leq j \leq i - 1$?

The reader interested in a detailed analysis of (2) with $\underline{f}_k \equiv \underline{0}$ is referred to [16]. For asymptotic behavior see [9].

With little change (2) could also be used to model migration between geographical areas instead of age groups.

5. THE LEONTIEF MODEL

The Leontief model is a dynamic model of a multisector economy. It is constructed as follows. Suppose the economy is divided into n sectors. Let $\underline{x}_k \in \mathbb{C}^n$ have i^{th} component the output in the kth time period of sector i. Let $\underline{d}_k \in \mathbb{C}^n$ have i^{th} component the final demand (demand in the kth time period excluding investment demand). Let b_{ij} be the amount of commodity i that sector j must have to produce one unit of commodity j. Let $B = [b_{ij}]$. Note that if a given sector does not produce a commodity that is utilized by others, (for example agriculture [40]), then B may have rows of zeros. Thus B is often singular. Let a_{ij} be the proportion of commodity j that gets transferred to commodity i in the kth time period. $A = [a_{ij}]$ is called the Leontief input-out matrix or the matrix of flow coefficients. The Leontief model then says that

> amount of commodity i = amount of commodity i inputed by all sectors + amount needed for production of the next output $\underline{x}(k + 1)$ + amount used to meet noninvestment demand (consumption). (1)

Note that a component of $\underline{x}_{k+1}$ could be lower than that of $\underline{x}_k$, if for example $\underline{d}_k$ is large. In matrix form (1) is $\underline{x}_k = A\underline{x}_k + B(\underline{x}_{k+1} - \underline{x}_k) + \underline{d}_k$, or

$$B\underline{x}_{k+1} + [A - B - I]\underline{x}_k = -\underline{d}_k \qquad (2)$$

While A,B could be functions of k, we shall assume they are constant. If B is singular, (2) is an equation of the type (1.2).

Equation (2) can be viewed as a deterministic or control problem. For example, future demand levels may be effected by government policies so that $\underline{d}_k$ could be altered to try and produce a desired $\underline{x}_{k+1}$. This then would be a singular control problem like those discussed in Section 2.

We refer the reader interested in more economic background to [40], [44], [48], [49], [50], [53] or their bibliographies.

Leontief [48, Chapter 3] has also proposed the continuous version of (2),

$$B\dot{\underline{x}} = (I - A)\underline{x} + \underline{d}. \qquad (3)$$

We shall see in Chapter 3, that (2) exhibits a forward time dependence while (3) does not. Moreover (3) is consistent for sufficiently smooth demand. The only difficulty with (3) is that part of $\underline{d}$ must be sufficiently differentiable and (3) is not consistent for all $\underline{x}(0)$ if B is singular. These problems can be avoided if impulsive solutions to (3) are allowed.

6. SINGULAR PERTURBATIONS

In many applications, a boundary value problem, denoted by P_ε, depends on a small positive parameter ε in such a way that the "full" differential equation $\varepsilon > 0$ is of higher order than the "reduced" equation obtained by setting $\varepsilon = 0$. Since the reduced equation is of lower order than the full equation, the solution of the reduced problem cannot be expected to satisfy all of the boundary conditions of the full problem. Thus, even if the limiting solution exists, uniform convergence cannot be expected near the boundary as $\varepsilon \to 0$. Such regions of non-uniform convergence are called <u>boundary layers</u> and are the distinguishing feature of singular perturbation problems.

Several questions arise:

(a) Does the solution of P_ε have a limit as $\varepsilon \to 0$?

(b) If a limiting solution exists, does it satisfy the reduced equation?

(c) If the limiting solution satisfies the reduced equation, what boundary conditions will be satisfied by the limiting solution?

(d) What are the asymptotic representations of the solution?

A classical example of a singular perturbation problem that is easy to visualize and illustrates the general behavior of almost all singular perturbation problems is the flow past a body at low viscosity. In viscous flow, the tangential velocity must be zero at the boundary of a body (no-slip condition), while in inviscid flow, the fluid can slide along the boundary. Thus if viscosity is neglected, the solution of this "reduced problem" will not approximate the actual viscous flow near the boundary. However, for small viscosity, the actual viscous flow will be closely approximated by the inviscid flow except in a narrow strip near the boundary. This narrow strip is often called Prandtl's "boundary layer." For this example, the governing differential equation is a non-linear partial differential equation, the Navier-Stokes equations. However, the methods of solution involve principles similar to those employed in singular perturbations of ordinary differential equations.

We shall be concerned with systems of the form

$$A(\varepsilon)\dot{\underline{x}} = C(\varepsilon)\underline{x} + \underline{f}. \tag{1}$$

Systems of the type (4) and generalizations of (4) to variable coefficients occur naturally in the analysis of linear dynamical systems with a finite dimensional state space. Such systems play an important role in engineering problems in mechanical, electrical, and chemical engineering. The parameter ε can represent various small quantities, for example; mass, moment of inertia, time constants, capacitances, inductances, or concentrations. When these small parameters are neglected ($\varepsilon = 0$), the reduced system

$$A\dot{\underline{x}} = C\underline{x} + \underline{f} \tag{2}$$

can be expected to have A a singular matrix since neglecting the small parameters results in a reduction of the system's "order."

Small coefficients of derivatives can create "stiff" differential equations. Singular perturbation techniques can be used to solve the smaller reduced problem and then build an approximate solution of the full problem. Singular perturbation techniques can also be used to examine slow and fast effects.

Singular perturbation techniques are also important in control theory. Wilde and Kokotovíc [65] give a development based on standard control theory-oriented assumptions: controllability, observability, and invertibility whenever needed.

Similarly Porter [60] assumes invertibility and controllability of the appropriate matrices as needed in studying $\dot{\underline{x}} = A\underline{x} + B\underline{z}$, $\varepsilon\dot{\underline{z}} = C\underline{z} + D\underline{u}$.

As to be expected the solution of (1) involves an exponential. In Chapter 5 we will develop expansions of various matrix exponentials in terms of ε and apply them to (1). We will then examine some particular singularly perturbed problems. For example, the relationship between the system

$$\dot{\underline{x}} = A_1(\varepsilon)\underline{x} + A_2(\varepsilon)\underline{y}$$
$$\varepsilon\dot{\underline{y}} = B_1(\varepsilon)\underline{x} + B_2(\varepsilon)\underline{y} \tag{3}$$

and the reduced system

$$\dot{\underline{x}} = A_1\underline{x} + A_2\underline{y}$$
$$\underline{0} = B_1\underline{x} + B_2\underline{y} \tag{4}$$

will be examined in detail, as well as the related process

$$\dot{\underline{x}} = A_1(\varepsilon)\underline{x} + A_2(\varepsilon)y + A_3(\varepsilon)\underline{u}$$
$$\varepsilon\dot{\underline{y}} = B_1(\varepsilon)\underline{x} + B_2(\varepsilon)\underline{y} + B_3(\varepsilon)\underline{u} \tag{5}$$

and its associated reduced problem,

$$\dot{\underline{x}} = A_1\underline{x} + A_2\underline{y} + A_3\underline{u}$$
$$\underline{0} = B_1\underline{x} + B_2\underline{y} + B_3\underline{u} \quad . \tag{6}$$

(5) - (6) is, of course, just the non-homogeneous form of (3) - (4).

3 $A\dot{x} + Bx = f$, algebraic solution

1. SQUARE COEFFICIENTS

This section will discuss how to solve

$$A\underline{\dot{x}} + B\underline{x} = \underline{f}, \tag{1}$$

and the initial value problem

$$A\underline{\dot{x}} + B\underline{x} = \underline{f},\ \underline{x}(t_o) = \underline{c} \tag{2}$$

when $A, B \in \mathbb{C}^{n\times n}$, $\underline{f}$ is a vector-valued function. These results originally appeared in [17], and an improved version in [16].

If A is nonsingular, then the classical theory applies and one has the following results:

I. The general solution of the homogeneous equation, $A\underline{\dot{x}} + B\underline{x} = \underline{0}$, is given by $\underline{x}(t) = e^{-A^{-1}Bt}\underline{q}$, $\underline{q} \in \mathbb{C}^n$.

II. The homogeneous initial value problem, $A\underline{\dot{x}} + B\underline{x} = \underline{0}$, $\underline{x}(t_o) = \underline{c}$, has the unique solution $\underline{x}(t) = e^{-A^{-1}B(t - t_o)}\underline{c}$.

III. The general solution of the inhomogeneous equation $A\underline{\dot{x}} + B\underline{x} = \underline{f}$, $\underline{f}$ continuous, is given by $\underline{x}(t) = e^{-A^{-1}Bt}\underline{q} + e^{-A^{-1}Bt}\int_a^t e^{A^{-1}Bs}A^{-1}\underline{f}(s)ds$, $a \in \mathbb{R}$, $\underline{q} \in \mathbb{C}^n$.

IV. The inhomogeneous initial value problem $A\underline{\dot{x}} + B\underline{x} = \underline{f}$, $\underline{x}(t_o) = \underline{c}$, $\underline{f}$ continuous, has the unique solution $\underline{x}(t) = e^{-A^{-1}B(t - t_o)}\underline{c} + \int_{t_o}^t e^{-A^{-1}B(t - s)}A^{-1}\underline{f}(s)ds$.

It is worth noting that (I) - (IV) do not depend on any deep results concerning ordinary differential equations but can be derived very quickly using the matrix exponential developed in Chapter 1. One just multiplies the differential equation $\dot{\underline{x}} + A^{-1}B\underline{x} = A^{-1}\underline{f}$ by $e^{A^{-1}Bt}$ to obtain $\frac{d}{dt}(e^{A^{-1}Bt}\underline{x}) = e^{A^{-1}Bt}A^{-1}\underline{f}$ and then integrates both sides.

When A is a singular matrix, things can happen that are impossible when A^{-1} exists. For example, the homogeneous initial value problem may be inconsistent, that is, there may not exist a solution. If there is a solution, it need not be unique.

Example 3.1.1 Consider $A\dot{\underline{x}} + B\underline{x} = \underline{0}$ where $A = \begin{bmatrix} 0 & 1 & 0 \\ 0 & 0 & 0 \\ 0 & 0 & 0 \end{bmatrix}$, $B = \begin{bmatrix} 0 & 0 & 1 \\ 0 & 0 & 0 \\ 1 & 0 & 0 \end{bmatrix}$.

The equations are $\dot{x}_2 + x_3 = 0$, $x_1 = 0$. The solutions are $x_1 = 0$, $x_2 = -\int_0^t x_3(t)dt + c$, x_3 arbitrary. Thus solutions exist only for initial points of the form $\underline{x}(0) = [0,\alpha,\beta]^T$ and solutions are not unique.

Example 3.1.2 The equations $\dot{x}_1 + x_2 = t$, $\dot{x}_1 + x_2 = t + 1$ are obviously inconsistent.

Example 3.1.3 Consider $A\dot{\underline{x}} + B\underline{x} = \underline{f}$ where $A = \begin{bmatrix} 1 & 0 & 0 \\ 0 & 0 & 1 \\ 0 & 0 & 0 \end{bmatrix}$, $B = I$. In component form we have $\dot{x}_1 + x_1 = f_1$, $\dot{x}_3 + x_2 = f_2$, $x_3 = f_3$. The first equation has a unique solution for any given f_1 and $x_1(0)$. If f_3 is differentiable, the solutions of the other two equations are $x_2 = f_2 - \dot{f}_3$, $x_3 = f_3$. Thus solutions exist if and only if f_3 is differentiable and the initial conditions are of the form $x_2(0) = \dot{f}_2(0) - f_3(0)$, $x_3(0) = f_3(0)$. If the solution exists, it is unique.

Definition 3.1.1 For $A,B \in \mathbb{C}^{n\times n}$ and $t_0 \in \mathbb{R}$, the vector $\underline{c} \in \mathbb{C}^n$ is said to be a consistent initial vector associated with t_0 for (2) if (2) possesses at least one solution. Equation (1) is said to be tractable at the point t_0 if the initial value problem (2) has a unique solution for each consistent initial vector, $\underline{c}$, associated with t_0.

If the homogeneous equation $A\dot{\underline{x}}(t) + B\underline{x}(t) = \underline{0}$ is tractable at some point $t_0 \in \mathbb{R}$, it is tractable at every $t \in \mathbb{R}$. So we may simply say the equation is tractable.

Much of this section will be based on the assumption that $\lambda A + B$ is invertible for some scalar λ. That is, $\lambda A + B$ is a "regular pencil" of matrices [28].

The following simple fact will be quite useful.

Lemma 3.1.1 Let $A,B \in \mathbb{C}^{n\times n}$. Suppose there exists a $\lambda \in \mathbb{C}$ such that $(\lambda A + B)^{-1}$ exists, and let $\hat{A}_\lambda = (\lambda A + B)^{-1}A$ and $\hat{B}_\lambda = (\lambda A + B)^{-1}B$. Then $\hat{B}_\lambda = I - \lambda\hat{A}_\lambda$ and hence $\hat{A}_\lambda\hat{B}_\lambda = \hat{B}_\lambda\hat{A}_\lambda$.

The notation $\hat{A}_\lambda$, $\hat{B}_\lambda$ will be used throughout this book.

This assumption is natural since

Theorem 3.1.1 For $A,B \in \mathbb{C}^{n\times n}$, the homogeneous differential equation

$$A\dot{\underline{x}}(t) + B\underline{x}(t) = \underline{0} \tag{3}$$

is tractable if and only if there exists a scalar $\lambda \in \mathbb{C}$ such that $(\lambda A + B)^{-1}$ exists.

Proof Suppose first there exists a $\lambda \in \mathbb{C}$ such that $(\lambda A + B)^{-1}$ exists. Let $\hat{A}_\lambda = (\lambda A + B)^{-1}A$, $\hat{B}_\lambda = (\lambda A + B)^{-1}B = I - \lambda\hat{A}$. Thus $A\dot{\underline{x}} + B\underline{x} = \underline{0}$ is tractable if and only if $\hat{A}_\lambda\dot{\underline{x}} + \hat{B}_\lambda\underline{x} = \underline{0}$ is tractable. There exists a nonsingular matrix T such that $T^{-1}A\,T = \begin{bmatrix} C & 0 \\ 0 & N \end{bmatrix}$, $T^{-1}B\,T = (I - \lambda A) = \begin{bmatrix} I - \lambda C & 0 \\ 0 & I - \lambda N \end{bmatrix}$ where C is nonsingular and N is nilpotent. Letting $\underline{x} = T\underline{y}$ the differential equation becomes

$$\begin{bmatrix} C & 0 \\ 0 & N \end{bmatrix}\begin{bmatrix} \dot{\underline{y}}_1 \\ \dot{\underline{y}}_2 \end{bmatrix} + \begin{bmatrix} I - \lambda C & 0 \\ 0 & I - \lambda N \end{bmatrix}\begin{bmatrix} \underline{y}_1 \\ \underline{y}_2 \end{bmatrix} = \begin{bmatrix} \underline{0} \\ \underline{0} \end{bmatrix} \text{ or}$$

$$C\dot{\underline{y}}_1 + (I - \lambda C)\underline{y}_1 = \underline{0} \ , \quad N\dot{\underline{y}}_2 + (I - \lambda N)\underline{y}_2 = \underline{0}. \tag{4}$$

The first equation in (4) is tractable since C is nonsingular. Thus it suffices to show that the second equation is tractable. Let $k = \text{Ind}(N)$. Multiplying the second equation of (4) by N^{k-1} we find $N^{k-1}\underline{y}_2 = \underline{0}$. Multiplying the second equation of (4) by N^{k-2} we find similarly that $N^{k-2}\underline{y}_2 = \underline{0}$. Continuing in this manner we find $\underline{y}_2 = \underline{0}$ and thus $N\dot{\underline{y}}_2 + (I - \lambda N)\underline{y}_2$ is tractable.

Suppose now that $A\dot{\underline{x}} + B\underline{x} = \underline{0}$ is tractable. We need to show that there is a $\lambda \in \mathbb{C}$ such that $\lambda A + B$ is invertible. Suppose that this is not true. Then $\lambda A + B$ is singular for all $\lambda \in \mathbb{C}$. This means that for each $\lambda \in \mathbb{C}$, there is a vector $\underline{v}_\lambda \in \mathbb{C}^n$ such that $(\lambda A + B)\underline{v}_\lambda = \underline{0}$ and $\underline{v}_\lambda \neq \underline{0}$. Let $\{\underline{v}_{\lambda_1}, \underline{v}_{\lambda_2}, \ldots, \underline{v}_{\lambda_s}\}$ be a finite linearly dependent set of such vectors. Let $\underline{x}_{\lambda_i}(t) = e^{\lambda_i t}\underline{v}_{\lambda_i}$ and let $\{\alpha_1, \alpha_2, \ldots, \alpha_s\} \subseteq \mathbb{C}$ be such that $\sum_{i=1}^{s} \alpha_i \underline{v}_{\lambda_i} = \underline{0}$, where not all the α_i's are 0. Then $\underline{z}(t) = \sum_{i=1}^{s} \alpha_i \underline{x}_{\lambda_i}(t)$ is not identically zero and is easily seen to be a solution of (3). However, $\underline{z}(0) = \sum_{i=1}^{s} \alpha_i \underline{v}_{\lambda_i} = \underline{0}$. Thus, there are two different solutions of (3), namely $\underline{z}(t)$ and $\underline{0}$, which satisfy the initial condition $\underline{x}(0) = \underline{0}$. Therefore, (3) is not tractable at $t = 0$ which contradicts our hypothesis. Hence, $(\lambda A + B)^{-1}$ exists for some $\lambda \in \mathbb{C}$. □

Note that $\lambda A + B$ being invertible is equivalent to being able to formally solve (2) by Laplace transforms. This approach will be utilized in Chapter 4.

The next theorem will be used to show that most of our later development is independent of the scalar λ which is used in the expression $(\lambda A + B)^{-1}$.

Theorem 3.1.2 Suppose that $A, B \in \mathbb{C}^{n\times n}$ are such that there exists a $\lambda \in \mathbb{C}$ so that $(\lambda A + B)^{-1}$ exists. Let $\hat{A}_\lambda = (\lambda A + B)^{-1}A$, $\hat{B}_\lambda = (\lambda A + B)^{-1}B$, and $\underline{\hat{f}}_\lambda = (\lambda A + B)^{-1}\underline{f}$ for $\underline{f} \in \mathbb{C}^n$. For all $\alpha, \mu \in \mathbb{C}$ for which $(\alpha A + B)^{-1}$ and $(\mu A + B)^{-1}$ exist, the following statements are true.

$$\hat{A}_\alpha \hat{A}_\alpha^D = \hat{A}_\mu \hat{A}_\mu^D. \tag{5}$$

$$\hat{A}_\alpha^D \hat{B}_\alpha = \hat{A}_\mu^D \hat{B}_\mu, \text{ and } \hat{A}_\alpha \hat{B}_\alpha^D = \hat{A}_\mu \hat{B}_\mu^D. \tag{6}$$

$$\mathrm{Ind}(\hat{A}_\alpha) = \mathrm{Ind}(\hat{A}_\mu) \text{ and } R(\hat{A}_\alpha) = R(\hat{A}_\mu). \tag{7}$$

$$\hat{A}_\alpha^D \underline{\hat{f}}_\alpha = \hat{A}_\mu^D \underline{\hat{f}}_\mu. \tag{8}$$

$$\hat{B}_\alpha^D \underline{\hat{f}}_\alpha = \hat{B}_\mu^D \underline{\hat{f}}_\mu. \tag{9}$$

Proof To prove (5), write $\hat{A}_\alpha^D \hat{A}_\alpha = [(\alpha A + B)^{-1}A]^D \hat{A}_\alpha = [(\alpha A + B)^{-1}(\mu A + B)$ $(\mu A + B)^{-1}A]^D \hat{A}_\alpha = [(\alpha\hat{A}_\mu + \hat{B}_\mu)^{-1}\hat{A}_\mu]^D \hat{A}_\alpha = \hat{A}_\mu^D(\alpha\hat{A}_\mu + \hat{B}_\mu)\hat{A}_\alpha$, (since $\hat{A}_\mu$, $\hat{B}_\mu$ commute) $= \hat{A}_\mu^D[(\mu A + B)^{-1}(\alpha A + B)]\hat{A}_\alpha = \hat{A}_\mu^D(\mu A + B)^{-1}(\alpha A + B)(\alpha A + B)^{-1}A$ $= \hat{A}_\mu^D \hat{A}_\mu$. The proof of (6) is similar and is left as an exercise. To prove (7), write $\hat{A}_\alpha = [(\alpha A + B)^{-1}(\mu A + B)](\mu A + B)^{-1}A = (\alpha\hat{A}_\mu + \hat{B}_\mu)^{-1}\hat{A}_\mu$ $= \hat{A}_\mu(\alpha\hat{A}_\mu + \hat{B}_\mu)^{-1}$. Since $\hat{A}_\mu$ and $\hat{B}_\mu$ commute, it follows that for each positive integer m, $R(\hat{A}_\alpha^m) = R(\hat{A}_\mu^m)$. Thus (7) follows. To prove (8), use the same technique used to prove (5) to obtain $\hat{A}_\alpha^D \underline{\hat{f}}_\alpha = [\hat{A}_\mu^D(\mu A + B)^{-1}$ $(\alpha A + B)]\underline{\hat{f}}_\alpha = \hat{A}_\mu^D(\mu A + B)^{-1}(\alpha A + B)(\alpha A + B)^{-1}\underline{f} = \hat{A}_\mu^D \underline{\hat{f}}_\mu$. The proof of (9) is similar. □

In view of the preceding theorem, we can now drop the subscript λ whenever the terms $\hat{A}_\lambda \hat{A}_\lambda^D$, $\hat{A}_\lambda^D \hat{B}_\lambda$, $R(\hat{A}_\lambda^m)$, $\mathrm{Ind}(\hat{A}_\lambda)$, $\hat{A}_\lambda^D \hat{\underline{f}}_\lambda$, and $\hat{B}_\lambda^D \hat{\underline{f}}_\lambda$ appear. We shall do so.

Let's return to the proof of Theorem 1. Recall that the original system $A\dot{\underline{x}} + B\underline{x} = \underline{0}$ is equivalent to the equations (4). The solutions of (4) are $\underline{y}_1 = e^{-C^{-1}(I - \lambda C)(t - t_o)}\underline{d}_1$, $\underline{d}_1$ arbitrary, and $\underline{y}_2 = \underline{0}$. In terms of the original variables we have

$$\underline{x}(t) = T\underline{y}(t) = T\begin{bmatrix} e^{-C^{-1}(I - \lambda C)(t - t_o)} & 0 \\ 0 & 0 \end{bmatrix} T^{-1}T\begin{bmatrix} I & 0 \\ 0 & 0 \end{bmatrix} T^{-1}T\begin{bmatrix} \underline{d}_1 \\ \underline{d}_2 \end{bmatrix}$$

$$= e^{-\hat{A}^D\hat{B}(t - t_o)}\hat{A}\hat{A}^D\underline{c}$$

where $\underline{c} = T[\underline{d}_1^*, \underline{d}_2^*]^* \in \mathbb{C}^n$ is arbitrary. Thus we have proved the first part of the following theorem.

<u>Theorem 3.1.3</u> Suppose $A\dot{\underline{x}} + B\underline{x} = \underline{0}$ is tractable. Then the general solution is given by

$$\underline{x}(t) = e^{-\hat{A}^D\hat{B}(t - t_o)}\hat{A}\hat{A}^D\underline{q}, \quad \underline{q} \in \mathbb{C}^n. \tag{10}$$

A vector $\underline{c} \in \mathbb{C}^n$ is a consistent initial vector for the homogeneous equation if and only if $\underline{c} = \hat{A}\hat{A}^D\underline{c}$ ($\underline{c} \in R(\hat{A}^k) = R(\hat{A}^D\hat{A})$), where $k = \mathrm{Ind}(\hat{A})$.

Suppose that $\underline{f}(t)$ is k-times continuously differentiable around t_o. Then the nonhomogeneous equation $A\dot{\underline{x}} + B\underline{x} = \underline{f}$ always possesses solutions and a particular solution is given by

$$\underline{x}(t) = e^{-\hat{A}^D\hat{B}t}\int_{t_o}^{t} e^{\hat{A}^D\hat{B}s}\hat{A}^D\hat{\underline{f}}(s)ds + (I-\hat{A}\hat{A}^D)\sum_{i=0}^{k-1}(-1)^i[\hat{A}\hat{B}^D]^i\hat{B}^D\hat{\underline{f}}^{(i)}(t). \tag{11}$$

Moreover, the expression (11) is independent of λ. The general solution is given by

$$\underline{x}(t) = e^{-\hat{A}^D\hat{B}(t - t_0)}\hat{A}\hat{A}^D\underline{q} + e^{-\hat{A}^D\hat{B}t}\int_{t_0}^{t} e^{\hat{A}^D\hat{B}s}\hat{A}^D\hat{\underline{f}}(s)ds$$

$$+ (I - \hat{A}\hat{A}^D)\sum_{i=0}^{k-1}(-1)^i[\hat{A}\hat{B}^D]^i\hat{B}^D\hat{\underline{f}}^{(i)}(t), \tag{12}$$

where $\underline{q} \in \mathbb{C}^n$. Let $\hat{\underline{w}} = (I - \hat{A}\hat{A}^D)\sum_{i=0}^{k-1}(-1)^i(\hat{A}\hat{B}^D)^i\hat{B}^D\hat{\underline{f}}^{(i)}(t)$. Then $\hat{\underline{w}}$ is independent of λ. A vector $\underline{c} \in \mathbb{C}^n$ is a consistent initial vector associated with $t_0 \in \mathbb{R}$ for the inhomogeneous equation if and only if $\underline{c}$ solves $(I - \hat{A}\hat{A}^D)(\underline{c} - \hat{\underline{w}}(0)) = \underline{0}$. Furthermore, the inhomogeneous equation is tractable at t_0 and the unique solution of the initial value problem with $\underline{x}(t_0) = \underline{c}$, $\underline{c}$ a consistent initial vector associated with t_0, is given by (12) with $\underline{q} = \underline{c}$.

Proof (12) will follow from (10) and (11). We have already shown (10). To see (11) let

$$\underline{x}_1 = \hat{A}^D e^{-\hat{A}^D\hat{B}t}\int_{0}^{t} e^{\hat{A}^D\hat{B}s}\underline{f}(s)ds, \quad \underline{x}_2 = (I - \hat{A}\hat{A}^D)\sum_{i=0}^{k-1}(-1)^i\hat{A}^i(\hat{B}^D)^{i+1}\hat{\underline{f}}^{(i)}(t),$$

where we have taken $t_0 = 0$ for notational convenience. We shall show that

$$\hat{A}\dot{\underline{x}}_1 + \hat{B}\underline{x}_1 = \hat{A}\hat{A}^D\underline{f} \quad \text{and} \tag{13}$$

$$\hat{A}\dot{\underline{x}}_2 + \hat{B}\underline{x}_2 = (I - \hat{A}\hat{A}^D)\underline{f}. \tag{14}$$

To verify (13), note that $\hat{A}\dot{\underline{x}}_1 = \hat{A}[-\hat{A}^D\hat{B}\underline{x}_1 + \hat{A}^D e^{-\hat{A}^D\hat{B}t}e^{\hat{A}^D\hat{B}t}\underline{f}] = -\hat{A}\hat{A}^D\hat{B}\underline{x}_1 + \hat{A}\hat{A}^D\underline{f}$ $= -\hat{B}\underline{x}_1 + \hat{A}\hat{A}^D\underline{f}$, as desired. We now verify (14). $\hat{A}\dot{\underline{x}}_2$ is

$$(I - \hat{A}\hat{A}^D)\sum_{i=0}^{k-1}(-1)^i(\hat{A}\hat{B}^D)^{i+1}\hat{\underline{f}}^{(i+1)}(t) = (I - \hat{A}\hat{A}^D)\hat{B}\hat{B}^D\sum_{i=1}^{k-1}(-1)^{i-1}(\hat{A}\hat{B}^D)^i\hat{\underline{f}}^{(i)}(t)$$

$= (I - \hat{A}\hat{A}^D)\hat{B} \sum_{i=1}^{k-1} (-1)^{i-1}\hat{A}^i(\hat{B}^D)^{i+1} \hat{\underline{f}}^{(i)}(t) = (I - \hat{A}\hat{A}^D)\hat{B}(-\underline{x}_2 + \hat{B}^D\hat{\underline{f}}) = -\hat{B}\underline{x}_2 +$
$(I - \hat{A}\hat{A}^D)\hat{B}\hat{B}^D\hat{\underline{f}} = -\hat{B}\underline{x}_2 + (I - \hat{A}\hat{A}^D)\hat{\underline{f}}$ where the fact that $\hat{B},\hat{B}^D,\hat{A},\hat{A}$ commute has been used freely. Thus, $\underline{x}_1 + \underline{x}_2$ is a particular solution as desired. The characterization of the consistent initial vectors for the inhomogeneous equation follow directly from (12). That the solutions are independent of λ follows from Theorem 2. □

Note that for tractable homogeneous equations the initial vector must satisfy $(I - \hat{A}\hat{A}^D)\underline{x}(t_o) = \underline{0}$ or $\underline{x}(t_o) \in R(\hat{A}^k)$. But then $(I - \hat{A}^D\hat{A})\underline{x}(t_o) = \underline{0}$ for all t so that $\underline{x}(t) \in R(\hat{A}^k)$ for all t. Similarly, for the non-homogeneous equation, the initial vector $\underline{x}(t_o)$ satisfies $(I - \hat{A}^D\hat{A})(\underline{x}(t_o) - \hat{\underline{w}}(t_o)) = \underline{0}$ so that $(I - \hat{A}^D\hat{A})(\underline{x}(t) - \underline{w}(t)) = \underline{0}$ or $\underline{x}(t) - \underline{w}(t) \in R(\hat{A}^k)$ for all t.

One does not actually need $\underline{f}$ is k-times differentiable, but rather only that $(I - \hat{A}\hat{A}^D)\hat{A}^i\underline{f}$ is i-times differentiable.

An important special case is when B is invertible. Then we may take $\lambda = 0$ and $\hat{A} = B^{-1}A$, $\hat{B} = I$, $\hat{\underline{f}} = B^{-1}\underline{f}$.

The Drazin inverse can sometimes be useful even when A is invertible. If $\underline{f}(s)$ is a constant vector $\underline{f}$, the general solution of $\dot{\underline{x}} + B\underline{x} = \underline{f}$ is given by $\underline{x} = [e^{-Bt}\int_a^t e^{Bs}ds]\underline{f} + e^{-Bt}\underline{x}(a)$. If B^{-1} exists, $\underline{x}$ is easily evaluated since $\int e^{Bs}ds = B^{-1}e^{Bs} + G$, $G \in \mathbb{C}^{n\times n}$. However, if B is singular, then the evaluation of $\int e^{Bs}ds$ is more difficult. The next result shows how to do it using the Drazin inverse.

<u>Theorem 3.1.4</u> If $B \in \mathbb{C}^{n\times n}$ and $\text{Ind}(B) = k$, then

$$\int e^{Bs}ds = B^De^{Bs} + (I - BB^D)s[I + \frac{Bs}{2!} + \frac{B^2s^2}{3!} + \ldots + \frac{B^{k-1}s^{k-1}}{k!}] + G, G \in \mathbb{C}^{n\times n}.$$

Theorem 4 is easily proved by differentiating both sides and using the series expansion of e^{Bs}. Note that if $\underline{f} \in \mathbb{C}^n$, then

$$B^D\underline{f} + t\sum_{n=1}^{k-1} \frac{(-1)^k(I - BB^D)t^kB^k}{(k-1)!}\underline{f}$$ is a polynomial solution of $\dot{\underline{x}} + B\underline{x} = \underline{f}$.

We shall now work out an example in some detail.

Example 3.1.5 Consider the homogeneous differential equation

$A\dot{\underline{x}} + B\underline{x} = \underline{0}$ where $A = \begin{bmatrix} 1 & 0 & -2 \\ -1 & 0 & 2 \\ 2 & 3 & 2 \end{bmatrix}$, $B = \begin{bmatrix} 0 & 1 & 2 \\ -27 & -22 & -17 \\ 18 & 14 & 10 \end{bmatrix}$. Note that A and B are both singular and do not commute. Since A + B turns out to be invertible we multiply on the left by $(A + B)^{-1}$ to get $\hat{A}\dot{\underline{x}} + \hat{B}\underline{x} = \underline{0}$ where

$$\hat{A} = (A + B)^{-1}A = \frac{1}{3}\begin{bmatrix} -3 & -5 & -4 \\ 6 & 5 & 2 \\ -3 & 2 & 10 \end{bmatrix}, \quad \hat{B} = I - \hat{A} = \frac{1}{3}\begin{bmatrix} 6 & 5 & 4 \\ -6 & -2 & 2 \\ 3 & -2 & 7 \end{bmatrix}.$$

Then $\hat{A}^D$ is computed to be $\frac{1}{27}\begin{bmatrix} -27 & -41 & -28 \\ 54 & 77 & 46 \\ -27 & -34 & -14 \end{bmatrix}$. The consistency condition for initial conditions $(I - \hat{A}\hat{A}^D)\underline{x}(0) = \underline{0}$ has only one independent equation, $9x_1(0) + 7x_2(0) + 5x_3(0) = 0$.

Since $\sigma(-\hat{A}^D\hat{B}) = \{0,0,2/3\}$, it is not difficult to compute the solutions

as $$\underline{x} = e^{-\hat{A}^D\hat{B}t}\underline{x}(0) = \frac{1}{18}\begin{bmatrix} 18 & 1 - e^{2t/3} & 2(1 - e^{2t/3}) \\ 0 & 26 - 8e^{2t/3} & 16(1 - e^{2t/3}) \\ 0 & 13(e^{2t/3} - 1) & 26e^{2t/3} - 8 \end{bmatrix}\begin{bmatrix} x_1(0) \\ x_2(0) \\ x_3(0) \end{bmatrix}.$$

The consistency condition can be used to eliminate one of the $x_i(0)$.

2. RECTANGULAR COEFFICIENT MATRICES

For many applications it is necessary to solve $A\dot{\underline{x}} + B\underline{x} = \underline{f}$ when A and B are rectangular matrices. If $A,B \in \mathbb{C}^{m\times n}$ and $m > n$ (more equations than unknowns), the system is called overdetermined, if $m < n$ (more unknowns than equations), the system is called underdetermined. We shall consider an important special case of each type.

If $\lambda A + B$ is one-to-one (full column rank), then $m \geq n$ and (unless $m = n$) the system is overdetermined. We shall see below that solutions, if they exist, are uniquely determined by initial conditions and we shall obtain formulas for the solutions when they exist. If $\lambda A + B$ is onto (full row rank), then $m \leq n$ and (unless $m = n$) the system is underdetermined. In this case, solutions always exist but are not unique.

First we consider the case when $\lambda A + B$ is one-to-one. Recall that this implies that $(\lambda A + B)^{\dagger}(\lambda A + B) = I$.

Theorem 3.2.1 Consider $A\dot{\underline{x}} + B\underline{x} = \underline{0}$ where $A, B \in \mathbb{C}^{m\times n}$. Then

(a) $A\dot{\underline{x}} + B\underline{x} = \underline{0}$ is tractable if and only if $\lambda A + B$ is one-to-one for some $\lambda \in \mathbb{C}$.

(b) If $\lambda A + B$ is one-to-one for some λ, then all solutions are given by $\underline{x} = e^{-\hat{A}^D\hat{B}t}\underline{q}$ where $\hat{A} = (\lambda A + B)^{\dagger}A$, $\hat{B} = (\lambda A + B)^{\dagger}B$ and $\underline{q}$ must satisfy

$$\underline{q} = \hat{A}\hat{A}^D\underline{q} \text{ and } [I - (\lambda A + B)(\lambda A + B)^{\dagger}]A\hat{A}^D\{\hat{A}^D\hat{B}\}^k\underline{q} = \underline{0},\ 0 \leq k \leq n-1. \quad (1)$$

Proof (a) Assume $\lambda A + B$ is one-to-one. Every solution of $A\dot{\underline{x}} + B\underline{x} = \underline{0}$ is a solution of $\hat{A}\dot{\underline{x}} + \hat{B}\underline{x} = \underline{0}$, but since $\lambda\hat{A} + \hat{B} = I$, the latter equation is tractable, therefore the original equation is also. The converse is proved as in Theorem 1.3. (b) If $\underline{x}$ is a solution of $A\dot{\underline{x}} + B\underline{x} = \underline{0}$, then $\underline{x}$ is a solution of $\hat{A}\dot{\underline{x}} + \hat{B}\underline{x} = \underline{0}$. But $\hat{A}\hat{B} = \hat{B}\hat{A}$ and $\lambda\hat{A} + \hat{B} = I$. Hence $\underline{x} = e^{-\hat{A}^D\hat{B}t}\hat{A}^D\hat{A}\underline{q}$ by Theorem 1.3. Substituting back in gives $[-A\hat{A}^D\hat{B}\hat{A}^D\hat{A} + B\hat{A}^D\hat{A}]e^{-\hat{A}^D\hat{B}t}\underline{q} = \underline{0}$ for all t. Thus $[-A\hat{A}^D\hat{B} + B\hat{A}\hat{A}^D]e^{-\hat{A}^D\hat{B}t}\underline{q} = \underline{0}$ for all t, or equivalently, $[B\hat{A} - A\hat{B}]\hat{A}^D[\hat{A}^D\hat{B}]^k\underline{q} = \underline{0}$ for $k = 0,1,2,\ldots$. But $A\hat{B} = A(\lambda A + B)^{\dagger}B =$ $A(\lambda A + B)^{\dagger}(\lambda A + B) - A(\lambda A + B)^{\dagger}\lambda A = A - \lambda A(\lambda A + B)^{\dagger}A = A - (\lambda A + B)(\lambda A + B)^{\dagger}A$ $+ B(\lambda A + B)^{\dagger}A = [I - (\lambda A + B)(\lambda A + B)^{\dagger}]A + B\hat{A}$. □

The restriction (1) is often needed.

Example 3.2.1 Let $A = \begin{bmatrix} 1 \\ 0 \end{bmatrix}$, $B = \begin{bmatrix} 0 \\ 1 \end{bmatrix}$. Then $\lambda A + B$ is one-to-one and $N(\lambda A + B) = N(A) \cap N(B) = \{\underline{0}\}$ for all λ. $A\dot{x} + Bx = \underline{0}$ has only $x = 0$ as a solution. Multiplying by $(\lambda A + B)^\dagger = (|\lambda|^2 + 1)^{-1}[\lambda, 1]$ we get $\lambda(|\lambda|^2 + 1)^{-1}\dot{x} + (|\lambda|^2 + 1)^{-1}x = 0$ which has the non-zero solutions $x = e^{-\lambda^{-1}t}q$. The conditions (1) show that we must have $q = 0$.

Conditions under which equation (1) is satisfied are given in the exercises.

If A (or B) is one-to-one, one may use $A^\dagger$ (or $B^\dagger$) in place of $(\lambda A + B)^\dagger$ in Theorem 1. For our applications B being one-to-one is of most interest. Note however that:

Theorem 3.2.2 $A\underline{\dot{x}} + B\underline{x} = \underline{0}$, $\underline{x}(0) = \underline{x}_o$ has unique solutions for all $\underline{x}_o$ if and only if A is one-to-one $(A^\dagger A = I)$ and $R(B) \subseteq R(A)$, $(AA^\dagger B = B)$.

Proof Assume $A^\dagger A = I$ and $AA^\dagger B = B$. Then $\underline{x}$ is a solution of $A\underline{\dot{x}} + B\underline{x} = \underline{0}$ if and only if $\underline{x}$ is a solution of $\underline{\dot{x}} + A^\dagger B\underline{x} = \underline{0}$. However $\underline{\dot{x}} + A^\dagger B\underline{x} = \underline{0}$ has unique solutions for all initial conditions.

Conversely, assume $A\underline{\dot{x}} + B\underline{x} = \underline{0}$ has unique solutions for all $\underline{x}_o$. Then by (1), $\hat{A}^D\hat{A}\underline{x}_o = \underline{x}_o$ for all $\underline{x}_o$. This gives $\hat{A} = (\lambda A + B)^\dagger A$, and hence A, is one-to-one. To see that $AA^\dagger B = B$, note that every solution of $A\underline{\dot{x}} + B\underline{x} = \underline{0}$, also satisfies $A\underline{\dot{x}} + AA^\dagger B\underline{x} = \underline{0}$ since $AA^\dagger A = A$. Thus $AA^\dagger B\underline{x} = B\underline{x}$ for all solutions $\underline{x}$. Since $\underline{x}(t_o)$ is arbitrary, we have $AA^\dagger B = B$ as desired. $\square$

Before solving

$$A\underline{\dot{x}} + B\underline{x} = \underline{f} \tag{2}$$

with $\lambda A + B$ one-to-one, we shall determine when (2) is consistent. Let $P = (\lambda A + B)(\lambda A + B)^\dagger$. Then (2) is equivalent to

$$PA\dot{\underline{x}} + PB\underline{x} = P\underline{f}, \tag{3}$$

$$(I - P)(A\dot{\underline{x}} + B\underline{x}) = (I - P)\underline{f}. \tag{4}$$

But (3) is equivalent to

$$\hat{A}\dot{\underline{x}} + \hat{B}\underline{x} = \hat{\underline{f}} \tag{5}$$

since $(\lambda A + B)^{\dagger}P = (\lambda A + B)^{\dagger}$. Now (5) is consistent by Theorem 1.3, and uniquely determines $\underline{x}$. Thus $(I - P)\underline{f}$ is determined by (4). Thus we have

Theorem 3.2.3 Suppose $\lambda A + B$ is one-to-one. Then all solutions of $A\dot{\underline{x}} + B\underline{x} = \underline{f}$, if any exist, are of the form

$$\begin{aligned}\underline{x} = {} & e^{-\hat{A}^D\hat{B}t}\hat{A}^D\hat{A}\underline{q} + \hat{A}^D e^{-\hat{A}^D\hat{B}t}\int_0^t e^{\hat{A}^D\hat{B}s}\hat{\underline{f}}(s)\,ds \\ & + (I - \hat{A}\hat{A}^D)\sum_{n=0}^{k-1}(-1)^n(\hat{A}\hat{B}^D)^n\hat{B}^D\hat{\underline{f}}^{(n)}\end{aligned} \tag{6}$$

where $\hat{A} = (\lambda A + B)^{\dagger}A$, $\hat{B} = (\lambda A + B)^{\dagger}B$, $k = \mathrm{Ind}(\hat{A})$, and $\hat{\underline{f}} = (\lambda A + B)^{\dagger}\underline{f}$. Let $P = (\lambda A + B)(\lambda A + B)^{\dagger}$. Then $A\dot{\underline{x}} + B\underline{x} = \underline{f}$ will be consistent if and only if

$$(I - P)\underline{f} = (I - P)(A\dot{\underline{x}} + B\underline{x}) \tag{7}$$

where $\underline{x}$ is given by (6).

There are several ways to use (7). In Theorem 1, $\underline{f}$ was given as zero and (7) was used to determine the consistent initial conditions. One could, on the other hand, view $\underline{x}(t_o)$ as given and use (7) to determine the consistent $\underline{f}$. In this case we have

Corollary 3.2.1 If $\lambda A + B$ is one-to-one and A, B are not square, then there exists $\underline{f}$ for which $A\dot{\underline{x}} + B\underline{x} = \underline{f}$ is inconsistent. In fact, for a given $\underline{x}(t_o)$ satisfying (1), there is a unique $\underline{f}$ for which $A\dot{\underline{x}} + B\underline{x} = \underline{f}$ is consistent and $P\underline{f} = \underline{0}$.

The case when $\lambda A + B$ is onto. Let A, B be $m \times n$ matrices. Let λ be such that $\lambda A + B$ is onto. Define $P = (\lambda A + B)^{\dagger}(\lambda A + B)$. Then $A\dot{\underline{x}} + B\underline{x} = \underline{f}$ becomes $AP\dot{\underline{x}} + BP\underline{x} = \underline{f} - A(I - P)\dot{\underline{x}} - B(I - P)\underline{x}$. Or, equivalently,

$$\begin{aligned} &A(\lambda A + B)^{\dagger}[(\lambda A + B)\dot{\underline{x}}] + B(\lambda A + B)^{\dagger}[(\lambda A + B)\underline{x}] \\ &= \underline{f} - A(I - P)\dot{\underline{x}} - B(I - P)\underline{x}. \end{aligned} \tag{8}$$

But $\lambda[A(\lambda A + B)^{\dagger}] + [B(\lambda A + B^{\dagger})] = I$. Thus (8) is, in terms of $(\lambda A + B)\underline{x}$, a differential equation of the type already solved and hence has a solution for any choice of $(I - P)\underline{x}$. Note that $[\lambda[A(\lambda A + B)^{\dagger}] + [B(\lambda A + B)^{\dagger}]]^{-1} = I$.

Theorem 3.2.4 Suppose that $\lambda A + B$ is onto and $\underline{f}$ is n-times differentiable. Let $\hat{A} = A(\lambda A + B)^{\dagger}$, $\hat{B} = B(\lambda A + B)^{\dagger}$, $P_{\lambda} = (\lambda A + B)^{\dagger}(\lambda A + B)$. Let $\underline{g} = \underline{f} - A[I - P]\dot{\underline{h}} - B(I - P)\underline{h}$ where $\underline{h}$ is an arbitrary $(n + 1)$-times differentiable vector valued function. Then all solutions of $A\dot{\underline{x}} + B\underline{x} = \underline{f}$ are of the form

$$\begin{aligned} \underline{x} = (\lambda A + B)^{\dagger}\{&e^{-\hat{A}^D\hat{B}t}\hat{A}\hat{A}^D\underline{q} + \hat{A}^D e^{-\hat{A}^D\hat{B}t}\int_0^t e^{\hat{A}^D\hat{B}s}\underline{g}(s)ds \\ &+ (I - \hat{A}^D\hat{A})\sum_{n=0}^{k-1}(-1)^n[\hat{A}\hat{B}^D]^n\hat{B}^D\underline{g}^{(n)}\} + [I - P]\underline{h}, \ \underline{q} \text{ an arbitrary} \end{aligned}$$

constant vector, $k = \mathrm{Ind}(\hat{A})$.

The formulas in Theorem 4 simplify considerably if A or B are onto. For our applications, the case when B is onto is the more important. If B is onto then one just sets $\lambda = 0$ in Theorem 4.

Theorem 3.2.6 Suppose that A is onto. Then all solutions of $A\dot{\underline{x}} + B\underline{x} = \underline{f}$ are of the form $\underline{x} = A^{\dagger}\{e^{-BA^{\dagger}t}\underline{q} + e^{-BA^{\dagger}t}\int_{o}^{t} e^{BA^{\dagger}s}\underline{g}(s)ds\} + [I - A^{\dagger}A]\underline{h}$ where $\underline{h}$ is an arbitrary function and $\underline{g} = \underline{f} - B[I - A^{\dagger}A]\underline{h}$.

Proof This one is easier to prove directly. Suppose A is onto and rewrite $A\dot{\underline{x}} + B\underline{x} = \underline{f}$ as $(A\dot{\underline{x}}) + BA^{\dagger}(A\underline{x}) = \underline{f} - B[I - A^{\dagger}A]\underline{x}$. Taking $[I - A^{\dagger}A]\underline{x}$ arbitrary we can solve uniquely for $A\underline{x}$, and use $\underline{x} = A^{\dagger}(A\underline{x}) + (I - A^{\dagger}A)\underline{x}$ to get the desired result. □

3. BOUNDARY VALUES

The preceding sections have developed most of the basic information we will need on the initial value problem. Of course, the same ideas may be applied to the boundary value problem

$$A\dot{\underline{x}} + B\underline{x} = \underline{f} \quad , \quad E\underline{x}(t_o) = \underline{a},\ F\underline{x}(t_1) = \underline{b}, \tag{1}$$

where $E \in \mathbb{C}^{m\times n}$, $F \in \mathbb{C}^{p\times n}$, $\underline{a} \in \mathbb{C}^{m}$, $\underline{b} \in \mathbb{C}^{p}$, $\underline{f}$ an n-times differentiable function on $[t_o,t_1]$. We shall assume $\lambda A + B$ is invertible, but a similar approach works on rectangular systems.

The classical assumptions are that A is invertible and rank $\begin{bmatrix} E \\ F \end{bmatrix} = n$. We shall assume neither. See [21] for a classical treatment.

The question of uniqueness is easier so we shall address it first.

Theorem 3.3.1 The following are equivalent.

(i) The boundary value problem (1), when consistent, has a unique solution.

(ii) The associated homogeneous boundary value problem

$$A\dot{\underline{x}} + B\underline{x} = \underline{0},\ E\underline{x}(t_o) = \underline{0},\ F\underline{x}(t_1) = \underline{0} \tag{2}$$

has only the zero solution.

(iii) $\text{Rank}(Q) = \text{rank}(\hat{A}^D\hat{A}) = \text{rank}(\hat{A}^n)$ where $\hat{A} = (\lambda A + B)^{-1}A$,

$$\hat{B} = (\lambda A + B)^{-1}B,\quad Q = \begin{bmatrix} E\hat{A}^D\hat{A} \\ Fe^{-\hat{A}^D\hat{B}(t_1 - t_o)}\hat{A}^D\hat{A} \end{bmatrix}.$$

Proof Since two solutions of (1) differ by a solution of (2), the equivalence of (i) and (ii) is immediate. Suppose then that $\underline{x}$ is a solution of (2). Then, by Theorem 1.3, $\underline{x} = e^{-\hat{A}^D\hat{B}(t - t_o)}\hat{A}^D\hat{A}\underline{q}$. To satisfy (1) is thus equivalent to

$$E\hat{A}^D\hat{A}\underline{q} = \underline{0} \quad , \quad Fe^{-\hat{A}^D\hat{B}(t_1 - t_o)}\hat{A}^D\hat{A}\underline{q} = \underline{0}. \tag{3}$$

But (3) will force $\hat{A}^D\hat{A}\underline{q} = \underline{0}$, precisely when (iii) holds so that (i), (ii), (iii) are equivalent. □

Suppose now that $\underline{x}$ is a solution of the differential equation in (1). Then from Theorem 1.3,

$$\hat{A}^D\hat{A}\underline{x} = e^{-\hat{A}^D\hat{B}(t - t_o)}\hat{A}^D\hat{A}\underline{q} + e^{-\hat{A}^D\hat{B}(t - t_o)}\int_{t_o}^{t} e^{\hat{A}^D\hat{B}s}\hat{A}^D\underline{\hat{f}}(s)ds, \tag{4}$$

$$(I - \hat{A}^D\hat{A})\underline{x} = (I - \hat{A}^D\hat{A})\sum_{i=0}^{k-1}(-1)^i[\hat{A}\hat{B}^D]^i\hat{B}^D\underline{\hat{f}}^{(i)}. \tag{5}$$

Let $\underline{h}(t) = (I - \hat{A}^D\hat{A})\underline{x}$. The boundary conditions in (1) become $E\hat{A}^D\hat{A}\underline{q}$ $+ E(I - \hat{A}^D\hat{A})\underline{h}(t_o) = \underline{a}$, $F\hat{A}^D\hat{A}e^{-\hat{A}^D\hat{B}(t_1 - t_o)}\hat{A}^D\hat{A}\underline{q} +$

$F\hat{A}^D\hat{A}e^{-\hat{A}^D\hat{B}(t_1 - t_o)} \int_{t_o}^{t_1} e^{\hat{A}\hat{B}s}\hat{A}^D\hat{\underline{f}}(s)ds + F(I - \hat{A}^D\hat{A})\underline{h}(t_1) = \underline{b}$. Thus we have the following;

Theorem 3.3.2 For a given $\underline{f},\underline{a},\underline{b}$ the boundary value problem is consistent if and only if

$$Q\underline{q} = \begin{bmatrix} \underline{a} - E\underline{h}(t_o) \\ \underline{b} - F\underline{h}(t_1) - F\hat{A}^D\hat{A}e^{-\hat{A}^D\hat{B}(t_1 - t_o)} \int_{t_o}^{t_1} e^{\hat{A}\hat{B}s}\hat{\underline{f}}(s)ds \end{bmatrix} \tag{6}$$

has a solution $\underline{q}$.

It is frequently desirable to have a theory of Green's functions when studying a class of boundary value problems. A corresponding development is also possible for singular problems, with the appropriate modifications.

So that the interested reader can easily compare our results with standard ones we shall derive a Green's function analagous to that of Cole [20]. To make notation similar we shall take $\underline{a} = \underline{0}$, $\underline{b} = \underline{0}$, and $E,F \in \mathbb{C}^{n\times n}$. Furthermore we shall assume as in [21] that the boundary conditions (1) are equivalent to $E\underline{x}(t_o) + F\underline{x}(t_1) = \underline{0}$. Finally, take $t_o = 0$, $t_1 = 1$. Note that our earlier development included more general boundary conditions than we now have.

Let $Y(t) = e^{-\hat{A}^D\hat{B}t}$. If $\underline{x}$ is a solution of (1), then $\underline{x} = \hat{A}^D\hat{A}\underline{x} + (I - \hat{A}^D\hat{A})\underline{x}$ and $\hat{A}^D\hat{A}\underline{x} = Y(t)\hat{A}^D\hat{A}\underline{q} + Y(t) \int_0^t Y^{-1}(s)\hat{A}^D\hat{\underline{f}}(s)ds$, while $(I - \hat{A}^D\hat{A})\underline{x}$ is still given by (5). The boundary conditions give

$$E\hat{A}^D\hat{A}\underline{q} + E(I - \hat{A}^D\hat{A})\underline{h}(0) + FY(1)\hat{A}^D\hat{A}\underline{q} + FY(1) \int_0^1 Y^{-1}(s)\hat{A}^D\hat{\underline{f}}(s)ds + F(I - \hat{A}^D\hat{A})\underline{h}(1) = \underline{0} \tag{7}$$

Thus, if (1) is consistent and solutions are unique, letting $R = E\hat{A}^D\hat{A} + FY(1)\hat{A}^D\hat{A}$ gives $\hat{A}^D\hat{A}\underline{q} = -R^\dagger FY(1)\int_0^1 Y^{-1}(s)\hat{A}^D\hat{\underline{f}}(s)ds$ $- R^\dagger(E\underline{h}(0) + F\underline{h}(1))$. Substituting into (2) gives

$$\hat{A}^D\hat{A}\underline{x} = -Y(t)\left(R^\dagger FY(1)\int_0^1 Y^{-1}(s)\hat{A}^D\hat{\underline{f}}(s)ds - R^\dagger(E\underline{h}(0) + F\underline{h}(1))\right)$$
$$+Y(t)\int_0^t Y^{-1}(s)\hat{A}^D\hat{\underline{f}}(s)ds.$$
$$= -Y(t)R^\dagger FY(1)\int_0^1 Y^{-1}(s)\hat{A}^D\hat{\underline{f}}(s)ds + Y(t)R^\dagger(E\underline{h}(0) + F\underline{h}(1))$$
$$+Y(t)R^\dagger E\int_0^t Y^{-1}(s)\hat{A}^D\hat{\underline{f}}(s)ds \quad +Y(t)R^\dagger FY(1)\int_0^t Y^{-1}(s)\hat{A}^D\hat{\underline{f}}(s)ds.$$

since $R^\dagger(E\hat{A}^D\hat{A} + FY(1)\hat{A}^D\hat{A})$ is the identity on $\mathcal{R}(\hat{A}^D) = \mathcal{R}(\hat{A}^D\hat{A})$ and $\hat{A}^D$ commutes with $Y^{-1}(s)$ and $Y(t)$. Thus $\hat{A}^D\hat{A}\underline{x} = Y(t)R^\dagger FY(1)\int_0^t Y^{-1}(s)\hat{A}^D\hat{\underline{f}}(s)ds$ $- Y(t)R^\dagger FY(1)\int_t^1 Y^{-1}(s)\hat{\underline{f}}(s)ds$, or $\hat{A}^D\hat{A}\underline{x} = \int_0^1 G(t,s)\hat{\underline{f}}(s)ds$ $+ Y(t)R^\dagger(E\underline{h}(0) + F\underline{h}(1))$ where

$$G(t,s) = \begin{cases} Y(t)R^\dagger FY(1)Y^{-1}(s)\hat{A}^D & \text{if } s < t \\ -Y(t)R^\dagger FY(1)Y^{-1}(s)\hat{A}^D & \text{if } s > t. \end{cases} \tag{8}$$

To express $Y(t)R^\dagger(E\underline{h}(0) + F\underline{h}(1)) + (I - \hat{A}^D\hat{A})\underline{x}(t)$ in terms of an integral operator we shall have to use delta functions. Let $\Delta(t) = (I - \hat{A}\hat{A})\sum_{i=0}^{k-1}[\hat{A}\hat{B}^D]^i\hat{B}^D\delta^{(i)}(t)$. Then $(I - \hat{A}^D\hat{A})\underline{x}(t) = \int_0^1 \Delta(s - t)\hat{\underline{f}}(s)ds$ while $Y(t)R^\dagger(E\underline{h}(0) + F\underline{h}(1)) = \int_0^1 Y(t)R^\dagger(E\Delta(s) + F\Delta(s - 1))\hat{\underline{f}}(s)ds$. Thus

$$\underline{x}(t) = \int_0^1 G(t,s)\hat{\underline{f}}(s)ds + \int_0^1 H(t,s)\hat{\underline{f}}(s)ds$$

where $G(t,s)$ is given by (8) and $H(t,s) = \Delta(s - t) + Y(t)R^\dagger(E\Delta(s) + F\Delta(s - 1))$.

4. FUNCTIONAL OR DELAY EQUATIONS

In many applications involving linear processes, there are delay effects. That is, the way the process changes is not only effected by the current state of the system but also the state at prior times.

As shown in Chapter 2, the system $A\dot{\underline{x}} + B\underline{x} = \underline{f}$ has many applications. It is to be expected then that an understanding of

$$A\dot{\underline{x}}(t) + B\underline{x}(t) = \sum_{i=0}^{p} C_i(t)\underline{x}(t - \tau_i) + \underline{f}(t) \tag{1}$$

should also find many applications. It is the purpose of this section to develop the basic theory of (1). For pedagogical reasons we shall take only one delay, and a constant C_0. The general case will be discussed at the end of this section. Without loss of generality we may assume that $t \geq 0$ and $\tau_0 = 1$. Thus (1) becomes

$$A\dot{\underline{x}}(t) + B\underline{x}(t) = C\underline{x}(t - 1) + \underline{f}(t) \quad , \quad t \geq 0. \tag{2}$$

First, let us review the situation if A is invertible. Then (2) can be assumed to be in the form

$$\dot{\underline{x}} + B\underline{x} = C\underline{x}(t - 1) + \underline{f}(t) \quad , \quad t \geq 0. \tag{3}$$

To uniquely determine the solution of (3) one must specify an arbitrary <u>initial function</u> $\underline{x}_0$ defined on $[-1,0]$ which we shall assume is continuous. Then there is a unique solution to (3), defined on $[0,1]$, so that $\underline{x}(0) = \underline{x}_0(0^-)$. Continuing in this manner, given the solution exists on $[0,n]$, (3) has a unique solution on $[n , n+1]$ such that $\underline{x}(n^+) = \underline{x}(n^-)$ and the solution exists on $[0 , n+1]$. Thus for (3), a unique continuous solution exists on $[-1,\infty)$ for any continuous specification of $\underline{x}$ on $[-1,0]$.

We shall consider (2) under the assumption that $\lambda A + B$ is invertible for some λ. The behavior of (2) is different from that of (3). As to be expected $\underline{x}$ can no longer be taken to be arbitrary on [0,-1].

Example 3.4.1 Take $A = \begin{bmatrix} 0 & 1 \\ 0 & 0 \end{bmatrix}$, $B = I$, $C = \begin{bmatrix} 1 & 0 \\ 1 & 0 \end{bmatrix}$, $\underline{f} = \underline{0}$, so that (2) becomes: $\dot{y}(t) + x(t) = x(t - 1)$, $y(t) = x(t - 1)$. Then if $x(t) \equiv 1$, $y(t) \equiv 0$ on $[-1,0]$, there is no continuous solution to (2) since the second equation requires $y(0^+) = 1$.

It is also possible to have continuous solutions only exist for a finite interval.

Example 3.4.2 Take $A = \begin{bmatrix} 0 & 1 \\ 0 & 0 \end{bmatrix}$, $B = I$, $C = I$, $\underline{f} = \begin{bmatrix} \sin(\pi t) \\ \sin(\pi t) \end{bmatrix}$ and $\underline{x}(t) = \begin{bmatrix} \sin(\pi t) \\ \sin(\pi t) \end{bmatrix}$ on $[-1,0]$. The equations (2) are $\dot{y} + x = x(t - 1) + \sin(\pi t)$ and $y = x(t - 1) + \sin(\pi t)$. On $[0,1]$, (2) becomes $\dot{y} + x = 0$, $y = 0$, so that the solution is $y = 0$, $x = 0$ which agree at 0 with the initial conditions on $[-1,0]$. On $[1,2]$, (2) becomes $\dot{y} + x = \sin\pi t$, $y = \sin\pi t$, so that $y = \sin\pi t$, $x = \sin\pi t - \pi\cos\pi t$. But then $x(1^+) \neq x(1^-)$. Thus for the initial conditions given, a solution exists only on $[-1,1]$.

If in (2), $\underline{f} = \underline{0}$, we get the associated homogeneous equation

$$A\dot{\underline{x}}(t) + B\underline{x}(t) = C\underline{x}(t - 1). \tag{4}$$

Clearly all solutions of (2) are of the form $\underline{x}_p + \underline{x}_h$ where $\underline{x}_p$ is a solution of (2) and $\underline{x}_h$ is an arbitrary solution of (4). We shall prove that (2) always has at least one initial condition for which (2) has a solution on $[-1,\infty)$. We shall then characterize all the consistent initial conditions of (4) both for $[-1,\infty)$ and $[-1,n)$ time periods.

Let $\{\underline{x}_n(t)\}$, $n \geq 0$, $\{\underline{f}_n(t)\}$, $n \geq 1$ be two sequences of infinitely differentiable functions defined on $[0,1]$. $\underline{x}_n(t)$ (respectively $\underline{f}_n(t)$) should be thought of as $\underline{x}$ (respectively $\underline{f}$) on $[n-1\ ,\ n]$. As will become clear during our proofs, infinite differentiability is a natural assumption since the existence of solutions often requires at least some components of $\underline{x}, \underline{f}$ to be infinitely differentiable at the integers.

The system (2) now becomes

$$A\dot{\underline{x}}_n + B\underline{x}_n = C\underline{x}_{n-1} + \underline{f}_n \quad , \quad n \geq 1, \quad \underline{x}_0 \text{ given.} \tag{5}$$

We seek to characterize those $\underline{x}_0(t)$ such that (5) has a solution $\{\underline{x}_\ell\}_{\ell=0}^{r}$ such that $\underline{x}_\ell(1) = \underline{x}_{\ell+1}(0)$.

From Theorem 1.3, for $n \geq 1$,

$$\begin{aligned} \underline{x}_n(t) &= \exp(-\hat{A}^D\hat{B}t)\hat{A}^D\hat{A}\underline{x}_n(0) + \hat{A}^D\exp(-\hat{A}^D\hat{B}t)\int_0^t \exp(\hat{A}^D\hat{B}s)[\hat{C}\underline{x}_{n-1}(s) \\ &\quad + \hat{\underline{f}}_n(s)]ds + (I - \hat{A}^D\hat{A})\sum_{m=0}^{k-1}[-\hat{A}\hat{B}^D]^m\hat{B}^D[\hat{C}\underline{x}_{n-1}^{(m)}(t) + \hat{\underline{f}}_n^{(m)}(t)]. \end{aligned} \tag{6}$$

where $\hat{A} = (\lambda A + B)^{-1}A$, $\hat{B} = (\lambda A + B)^{-1}B$, $\hat{C} = (\lambda A + B)^{-1}C$, $\hat{\underline{f}}_n = (\lambda A + B)^{-1}\underline{f}_n$, and k is the index of $\hat{A}$. Since we need to manipulate this expression a lot, let $P = \hat{A}^D\hat{A}$, $Q = \hat{A}^D\hat{B}$, and $H = -\hat{A}\hat{B}^D$. Note that P is a projection and P, Q, H all commute. Thus we have

$$\begin{aligned} \underline{x}_n(t) &= \exp(-Qt)P\underline{x}_n(0) + \hat{A}^D\exp(-Qt)\int_0^t \exp(Qs)[\hat{C}\underline{x}_{n-1}(s) + \hat{\underline{f}}_n(s)]ds \\ &\quad + (I - P)\sum_{m=0}^{k-1} H^m\hat{B}^D[\hat{C}\underline{x}_{n-1}^{(m)}(t) + \hat{\underline{f}}_n^{(m)}(t)]. \end{aligned} \tag{7}$$

Regardless of what $\underline{x}_{n-1}$ is, letting $P\underline{x}_n(0) = P\underline{x}_{n-1}(1)$ makes $P\underline{x}$ continuous at n. The difficulty is with $(I - P)\underline{x}$ at n.

That $(I - P)\underline{x}_1(0) = (I - P)\underline{x}_o(1)$ gives

$$(I - P)\underline{x}_o(1) = (I - P) \sum_{m=0}^{k-1} H^m \hat{B}^D[\hat{C}\underline{x}_o^{(m)}(0) + \hat{\underline{f}}_1^{(m)}(0)]. \tag{8}$$

We shall show that given $\underline{f}$ and any $\{\underline{x}_o^{(m)}(0)\}$, $m \geq 0$ we can get a solution by specifying $\underline{x}_o^{(m)}(1)$. Take (8) as the definition of $(I - P)\underline{x}_o(1)$. For $n \geq 1$, $(I - P)\underline{x}_n(t) = (I - P) \sum_{m=0}^{k-1} H^m \hat{B}^D[\hat{C}\underline{x}_{n-1}^{(m)}(t) + \hat{\underline{f}}_n^{(m)}(t)]$. Thus the requirement that $(I - P)\underline{x}_n(0) = (I - P)\underline{x}_{n-1}(1)$, $n \geq 2$, is

$$(I - P) \sum_{m=0}^{k-1} H^m \hat{B}^D \hat{C}\left(\underline{x}_{n-1}^{(m)}(0) - \underline{x}_{n-2}^{(m)}(1)\right) = \underline{0} \tag{9}$$

since $\hat{\underline{f}}_n^{(m)}(0) = \hat{\underline{f}}_{n-1}^{(m)}(1)$, $m \geq 0$, $n \geq 2$. From (7), for $n \geq 1$, $r \geq 1$,

$$\begin{aligned} \underline{x}_n^{(r)}(t) = {} & (-Q)^r \exp(-Qt) P\underline{x}_n(0) \\ & + \hat{A}^D(-Q)^r \exp(-Qt) \int_0^t \exp(Qs)[\hat{C}\underline{x}_{n-1}(s) + \hat{\underline{f}}_n(s)]ds \\ & + \hat{A}^D \sum_{\ell=0}^{r-1} Q^{r-1-\ell}(\hat{C}\underline{x}_{n-1}^{(\ell)}(t) + \hat{\underline{f}}_n^{(\ell)}(t)) \\ & + (I - P) \sum_{m=0}^{k-1} H^m \hat{B}^D[\hat{C}\underline{x}_{n-1}^{(m+r)}(t) + \hat{\underline{f}}_n^{(m+r)}(t)]. \end{aligned} \tag{10}$$

In particular,

$$\begin{aligned} \underline{x}_1^{(r)}(0) = {} & (-Q)^r P\underline{x}_1(0) + \hat{A}^D \sum_{\ell=0}^{r-1} Q^{r-1-\ell}[\hat{C}\underline{x}_o^{(\ell)}(0) + \hat{\underline{f}}_1^{(\ell)}(0)] \\ & + (I - P) \sum_{m=0}^{k-1} H^m \hat{B}^D[\hat{C}\underline{x}_o^{(m+r)}(0) + \hat{\underline{f}}_1^{(m+r)}(0)]. \end{aligned} \tag{11}$$

Define $\underline{x}_o^{(r)}(1) = \underline{x}_1^{(r)}(0)$, where $\underline{x}_1^{(r)}(0)$ is given by (11). That an infinitely differentiable function on [0,1] exists for arbitrary $\{\underline{x}^{(r)}(0)\}$, $\{\underline{x}^{(r)}(1)\}$ follows from [34, Lemma 13.1, p. 261]. Let $\underline{x}_o(t)$ be such a function. We shall show that this is a consistent initial condition. Given this $\underline{x}_o$, we have $\underline{x}_1$ computed and by construction $\underline{x}_o^{(m)}(1) = \underline{x}_1^{(m)}(0)$, $m \geq 1$. Suppose then that we have $\underline{x}_o,\ldots,\underline{x}_n$ and

$$\underline{x}_r^{(m)}(1) = \underline{x}_{r+1}^{(m)}(0), \quad m \geq 0, \quad r \leq n-1. \tag{12}$$

We shall show that we get a similar $\underline{x}_{n+1}$. By (12) we see that (9) is satisfied. The definition of $P\underline{x}_{n+1}$ in terms of (6), the infinite differentiability of $\underline{f}$, and the induction hypothesis (12) applied to (10) means that $\underline{x}_n^{(m)}(1) = \underline{x}_{n+1}^{(m)}(0)$ so that the induction is complete. Thus we have proved the following theorem.

Theorem 3.4.1 If $\underline{f}$ is infinitely differentiable on $[0,\infty)$ and $\{\underline{x}_o^{(m)}(0)\}$ is an arbitrary sequence of numbers, and $\underline{x}_o(t)$ is any infinitely differentiable function on $[0,1]$ with these derivatives at zero such that $\underline{x}_o^{(m)}(1)$ is given by (11), then (2) is consistent and has an infinitely differentiable solution.

Let $\mathcal{C}$ be the space of $\mathbb{C}^n$-valued infinitely differentiable functions on $[0,1]$ with the family of semi-norms $\rho_m(\underline{f}) = \sup_{0\leq t\leq 1} \|\underline{f}^{(m)}(t)\|$. For any integer n, let $\mathcal{C}_n$ be those initial conditions $\underline{x}_o(t)$ in $\mathcal{C}$ for which a continuous solution to (4) exists on $[0,n]$.

Theorem 3.4.2 Each $\mathcal{C}_n$ is a closed subspace of $\mathcal{C}$, $\mathcal{C}_n \supseteq \mathcal{C}_{n+1}$. The set of consistent initial conditions $\mathcal{C}_\infty = \bigcap_{n=1}^{\infty} \mathcal{C}_n$ is an infinite dimensional closed subspace of $\mathcal{C}$.

Proof Using (7) and (9) we see that each $\mathcal{C}_n$ consists of those $\underline{x}_o \in \mathcal{C}$ whose derivatives at 0 and 1 satisfy n relationships. For example $\mathcal{C}_1$

consists of those which satisfy $(I - P) \sum_{m=0}^{k-1} H^m \hat{B}^D \hat{C} \underline{x}_o^{(m)}(0) = (I - P)\underline{x}_o(1)$,

while C_2 consists of those $\underline{x}_o$ which also satisfy
$(I - P) \sum_{m=0}^{k-1} H^m \hat{B}^D \hat{C} (\underline{x}_o^{(m)}(1) - \underline{x}_1^{(m)}(0)) = \underline{0}$. That is,

$$(I - P) \sum_{m=0}^{k-1} H^m \hat{B}^D \hat{C} \{ \underline{x}_o^{(m)}(1) - (-Q)^m P\underline{x}_o(1) + \hat{A}^D \sum_{\ell=0}^{m-1} Q^{m-1-\ell} \hat{C}\underline{x}_o^{(\ell)}(0)$$
$$+ (I - P) \sum_{\ell=0}^{k-1} H^\ell \hat{B}^D \hat{C} \underline{x}_o^{(\ell+m)}(0) \} = \underline{0}.$$

That C_n is closed follows from the continuity of evaluation of derivatives in C. That C_n is infinite dimensional follows from Theorem 1. □

Example 3.4.3 Take $A = 0$, $B = I$, $C = I$. Then (4) becomes $\underline{x}(t) = \underline{x}(t - 1)$. Thus C_1 consists of those $\underline{x}$ such that $\underline{x}_o(1) = \underline{x}_o(0)$. But if $\underline{x}_o \in C_1$, then (4) has a continuous solution. Hence $C_1 = C_n$ for all $n \geq 1$ and C_∞ is of finite co-dimension in C.

Example 3.4.4 Take, as in Example 1, $A = \begin{bmatrix} 0 & 1 \\ 0 & 0 \end{bmatrix}$, $B = I$, $C = \begin{bmatrix} 1 & 0 \\ 1 & 0 \end{bmatrix}$, and $\underline{x} = \begin{bmatrix} y \\ z \end{bmatrix}$ so that the system (4) is $\dot{z}_n + y_n = y_{n-1}$ or $y_n = y_{n-1} - \dot{z}_n$ and $z_n = y_{n-1}$. The requirement for C_1 is $z_o(1) = y_o(0)$, and $y_o(1) = y_o(0) - \dot{z}_o(0)$. Note that if z,y are continuous at n, then z is automatically continuous at n + 1. Thus the only condition is $y_n = y_{n-1} - \dot{z}_n = y_{n-1} - \dot{y}_{n-1}$, $n \geq 2$. Clearly the requirement $y_n(1) = y_{n+1}(0)$ places a nontrivial requirement on the first n + 1 derivatives of y_o so that $C_{n+1} \subsetneq C_n$ for $n \geq 1$.

For $A\dot{\underline{x}} + B\underline{x} = \underline{f}$, the assumption that $\lambda A + B$ was invertible for some scalar λ was equivalent to consistent initial conditions uniquely determining solutions. For the delay equation (2), the situation is more complicated. The existence of λ is equivalent to $\underline{x}_n$ and $\underline{f}_n$ uniquely determining $\underline{x}_{n+1}$ but that is different from $\underline{x}_0$ and $\underline{f}$ uniquely determining the $\underline{x}_n$. Intuitively $\lambda A + B$ being invertible is a "Markov" type of property. The state at "time" n + 1 depends only on the immediately preceding values $\underline{x}_n$, f_n.

Example 3.4.5 Let $A = 0$, $B = 0$, $C = \begin{bmatrix} 1 & 0 \\ 0 & 1 \end{bmatrix}$ so that $\lambda A + B$ is always singular. The system (2) is $\underline{x}_{n-1} = -\underline{f}_n$. There is a unique solution, namely $-\underline{f}(t + 1)$, and a single consistent initial condition $\underline{x}_0 = \underline{f}_1$ so that consistent initial conditions uniquely determine solutions. Note that $\underline{x}_{n+1}$ cannot be determined from $\underline{x}_n$ and $\underline{f}_n$ but depends on the future value $\underline{f}_{n+1}$.

Example 3.4.6 Let $A = 0$, $B = 0$, $C = \begin{bmatrix} 1 & 0 \\ 0 & 0 \end{bmatrix}$. If $(I - C)\underline{f} \neq \underline{0}$, then (2) has no consistent initial conditions at all. Let $\underline{f} = \begin{bmatrix} -g \\ 0 \end{bmatrix}$, $\underline{x} = \begin{bmatrix} y \\ z \end{bmatrix}$. Then $y(t) = g(t + 1)$ and $z(t)$ is an arbitrary function on $[-1,\infty)$. Clearly there exist distinct choices for z which agree on $[-1,0]$. Thus, in this example, solutions are not uniquely determined by consistent initial conditions.

The preceding examples illustrate several points. While the infinitely differentiable initial conditions were the appropriate space for the general problem on $[0,\infty)$, if the reader is interested in existence on $[0,n)$, then only $n(k - 1)$ differentiability is needed. Also, in the context of a particular problem as low as $k - 1$ times differentiability of some components of $\underline{f}$ and $\underline{x}_0$ will suffice.

We assumed that C was constant. However, this was not necessary to apply Theorem 1.3. If C is $k - 1$ times differentiable, then one may still apply Theorem 1.3 to get a formula like (6) except that $\hat{C}\underline{x}_{n-1}{}^{(m)}(t)$ is replaced by $(\hat{C}(t)\underline{x}_{n-1}(t))^{(m)}$. Of course, in general one may need as much as $n(k - 1)$ times differentiability of C on $[0,n)$ and infinite differentiability on $[0,\infty)$.

Similarly, the complication caused by several delays is that the consistent initial conditions must satisfy derivative conditions at points other than the end points. For example, consider

$$A\dot{\underline{x}}(t) + B\underline{x}(t) = C\underline{x}(t - 1) + D\underline{x}(t - 3) + \underline{f}(t). \tag{13}$$

Initial conditions are now defined on $[0,3]$. There are different ways to handle (13). One way is to take the $\underline{x}_n(t)$ on $[0,1]$, consider $\underline{x}_0$, $\underline{x}_1$, $\underline{x}_2$ arbitrary and write (18) as $A\dot{\underline{x}}_n + B\underline{x}_n = C\underline{x}_{n-1} + D\underline{x}_{n-3} + \underline{f}_n$. Of course, if the delays are not integer multiples of each other, then the computations will be messier, but are in principle the same.

5. APPLICATION TO CONTROL PROBLEMS

To illustrate how one can use the results of Sections 1 and 2, we shall solve the Basic Quadratic Cost Problem of Section 2.2. Recall that we had the process

$$\dot{\underline{x}} = A\underline{x} + B\underline{u}, \quad t_0 \leq t \leq t_1, \quad \underline{x}(t_0) = \underline{x}_0, \quad \underline{x}(t_1) = \underline{x}_1 \tag{1}$$

and cost

$$J[\underline{x},\underline{u}] = \frac{1}{2}\int_{t_0}^{t_1} (H\underline{x},\underline{x}) + (Q\underline{u},\underline{u})dt. \tag{2}$$

The necessary condition for a minimum was

$$\begin{bmatrix} I & 0 & 0 \\ 0 & I & 0 \\ 0 & 0 & 0 \end{bmatrix} \begin{bmatrix} \dot{\underline{\lambda}} \\ \dot{\underline{x}} \\ \dot{\underline{u}} \end{bmatrix} + \begin{bmatrix} A^* & H & 0 \\ 0 & -A & -B \\ B^* & 0 & Q \end{bmatrix} \begin{bmatrix} \underline{\lambda} \\ \underline{x} \\ \underline{u} \end{bmatrix} = \begin{bmatrix} \underline{0} \\ \underline{0} \\ \underline{0} \end{bmatrix}. \tag{3}$$

We shall first show that if (2) has a solution satisfying the boundary conditions, then $\underline{u}$ must be an optimal control.

Theorem 3.5.1 Suppose that $\underline{x}$, $\underline{u}$, $\underline{\lambda}$ is a solution of (3) and $\underline{x}(t_0) = \underline{x}_0$, $\underline{x}(t_1) = \underline{x}_1$. Then $\underline{u}$ is an optimal control.

Proof To show that $J[\hat{\underline{x}},\hat{\underline{u}}] \geq J[\underline{x},\underline{u}]$ for all $\hat{\underline{x}},\hat{\underline{u}}$ satisfying (1) is clearly equivalent to showing that $\phi(s) = J[s\underline{x} + (1 - s)\hat{\underline{x}},\ s\underline{u} + (1 - s)\hat{\underline{u}}]$ has a minimum at $s = 1$ for all $\hat{\underline{x}},\hat{\underline{u}}$. Let $J_0 = \frac{1}{2}\int_{t_0}^{t} (H\underline{x},\hat{\underline{x}}) + (Q\underline{u},\hat{\underline{u}})dt$, $\hat{J} = J[\hat{x},\hat{u}]$, and $J = J[\underline{x},\underline{u}]$. Then a direct calculation gives $\phi(s) = s^2(J - 2J_0 + \hat{J}) + s(2J_o - 2\hat{J}) + \hat{J}$. Since ϕ is quadratic in s it has a maximum or minimum at $s = 1$ if and only if $J_0 = J$, or equivalently,

$$\int_{t_0}^{t_1} (H\underline{x},\hat{\underline{x}}) + (Q\underline{u},\hat{\underline{u}})dt = \int_{t_0}^{t_1} (H\underline{x},\underline{x}) + (Q\underline{u},\underline{u})dt. \tag{4}$$

However, $\phi(s) \geq 0$ for all s so that if (4) holds there must be a minimum. Using the fact that $\hat{\underline{x}},\hat{\underline{u}}$ satisfies (1) and $\underline{\lambda},\underline{x},\underline{u}$ satisfies (3) it is straightforward to verify that (4) holds. The details, which we leave to the reader may be found in [11] or [16]. □

Note that solutions of (3) satisfying the boundary conditions provide optimal controls even if the differential equation (3) has non-unique solutions for consistent initial conditions. Of course, in that case, the optimal controls may not be unique.

A useful by-product of the proof of Theorem 1 is that

$$J[\underline{x},\underline{u}] = -2(\underline{\lambda},\underline{x}) \Big|_{t_0}^{t_1} . \tag{5}$$

To simplify the solving of (3) rewrite it as

$$\mathcal{A}\dot{\underline{z}} + \mathcal{B}\underline{z} = \underline{0} \tag{6}$$

where $\mathcal{A} = \begin{bmatrix} I & 0 \\ 0 & 0 \end{bmatrix}$, $\mathcal{B} = \begin{bmatrix} B_1 & B_2 \\ B_3 & B_4 \end{bmatrix}$. Here I is 2n × 2n,

$$B_1 = \begin{bmatrix} A^* & H \\ 0 & -A \end{bmatrix}, \; B_2 = \begin{bmatrix} 0 \\ -B \end{bmatrix}, \; B_3 = [B^* \;\; 0], \text{ and } B_4 = Q. \tag{7}$$

Clearly $(\mu + B_1)^{-1}$ exists except for a finite number of μ. Define

$$Q_\mu = B_4 - B_3(\mu + B_1)^{-1}B_2. \tag{8}$$

We now need the following easily verified result whose proof we omit.

<u>Proposition 3.5.1</u> $\mu\mathcal{A} + \mathcal{B}$ is invertible almost always if and only if Q_μ is invertible almost always.

Assume that μ, $\mathcal{A}$, $\mathcal{B}$ are such that $\mu\mathcal{A} + \mathcal{B}$, Q_μ, $\mu + B_1$ are invertible. Let $\hat{A} = (\mu\mathcal{A} + \mathcal{B})^{-1}\mathcal{A}$, $\hat{B} = (\mu\mathcal{A} + \mathcal{B})^{-1}\mathcal{B}$. Then N_μ, M_μ, Z_μ are defined by $\hat{A} = \begin{bmatrix} N_\mu & 0 \\ M_\mu & 0 \end{bmatrix}$, $\hat{B} = \begin{bmatrix} Z_\mu & 0 \\ -\mu M_\mu & I \end{bmatrix}$, and $\hat{A}^D = \begin{bmatrix} N_\mu^D & 0 \\ M_\mu N_\mu^{D^2} & 0 \end{bmatrix}$ [16, page 139] (this is Exercise 1.7.3). Hence $\hat{A}^D\hat{B} = \begin{bmatrix} N_\mu^D Z_\mu & 0 \\ M_\mu N_\mu^{D^2} Z_\mu & 0 \end{bmatrix}$,

$e^{-\hat{A}^D\hat{B}t} = \begin{bmatrix} e^{-[N_\mu^D Z_\mu]t} & 0 \\ M_\mu N_\mu^D\{e^{-[N_\mu^D Z_\mu]t} - I\} & I \end{bmatrix}$. Using Theorem 1.3 we see that the general solution of (6) is

$$e^{-\hat{A}^D\hat{B}t}\hat{A}^D\hat{A} = \begin{bmatrix} e^{-[N_\mu^D Z_\mu]t} N_\mu^D N_\mu & 0 \\ M_\mu N_\mu^D e^{-[N_\mu^D Z_\mu]t} & 0 \end{bmatrix}.$$

From the original equation (4) we have that

$$\begin{bmatrix} \underline{\lambda} \\ \underline{x} \end{bmatrix} = e^{-[N_\mu{}^D Z_\mu](t - t_0)} N_\mu{}^D N_\mu \begin{bmatrix} \underline{\lambda}_0 \\ \underline{x}_0 \end{bmatrix}, \text{ where } \underline{\lambda}_0 = \underline{\lambda}(t_0), \tag{9}$$

and

$$\underline{u} = M_\mu N_\mu{}^D \begin{bmatrix} \underline{\lambda} \\ \underline{x} \end{bmatrix}. \tag{10}$$

Thus we have shown that

Theorem 3.5.2 If Q_μ is invertible, then the optimal control $\underline{u}$ is given in terms of $\underline{x},\underline{\lambda}$ by (10) if an optimal control exists.

While (9) gives $\begin{bmatrix} \underline{\lambda} \\ \underline{x} \end{bmatrix}$ explicitly, (9) and (10) do not give $\underline{u}$ directly in terms of $\underline{x}$. We now turn to this problem. Let

$E(t) = e^{-[N_\mu{}^D Z_\mu](t - t_0)} N_\mu{}^D N_\mu = \begin{bmatrix} E_1(t) & E_2(t) \\ E_3(t) & E_4(t) \end{bmatrix}$ where the $E_i(t)$, $i = 1,2,3,4$ are all $n \times n$ matrices. Suppose that (3) has a solution. Let $\underline{\lambda}(t_0) = \underline{\lambda}_0$. Then $\begin{bmatrix} \underline{\lambda}(t) \\ \underline{x}(t) \end{bmatrix} = E(t)\begin{bmatrix} \underline{\lambda}_0 \\ \underline{x}_0 \end{bmatrix}$. Note that this is possible if and only if $\begin{bmatrix} \underline{\lambda}_0 \\ \underline{x}_0 \end{bmatrix}$ is in $\mathcal{R}(N_\mu{}^D N_\mu)$. Now $\begin{bmatrix} \underline{\lambda}(t_1) \\ \underline{x}(t_1) \end{bmatrix} = E(t_1)\begin{bmatrix} \underline{\lambda}_0 \\ \underline{x}_0 \end{bmatrix}$ or

$$\underline{x}_1 = E_3(t_1)\underline{\lambda}_0 + E_4(t_1)\underline{x}_0. \tag{11}$$

Once $\underline{\lambda}_0,\underline{x}_0$ are known, $\underline{x},\underline{u}$ follow from (9), (10), and (11).

On the other hand if (11) is viewed as defining $\underline{x}_1$, then from (9) $\underline{x}$ will go from $\underline{x}_0$ to $\underline{x}_1$. Thus we have established the following result.

Theorem 3.5.3 Suppose that Q_μ is invertible almost always. For a given $\underline{x}_o, \underline{x}_1$ there is an optimal control that takes $\underline{x}$ from $\underline{x}_o$ to $\underline{x}_1$ in the time interval $[t_o, t_1]$ if and only if the equation (11) has a solution $\underline{\lambda}_o$ such that $\begin{bmatrix} \underline{\lambda}_o \\ \underline{x}_o \end{bmatrix} \varepsilon \mathcal{R}(N_\mu^D N_\mu)$.

It is possible, under our assumptions, for $\underline{x}$ to be able to go from $\underline{x}_o$ to $\underline{x}_1$ but not have an optimal control existing if $(I - N_\mu^D N_\mu)\begin{bmatrix} \underline{\lambda}_o \\ \underline{x}_o \end{bmatrix} = \underline{0}$, $\underline{\lambda}_o$ satisfying (11), is inconsistent in $\underline{\lambda}_o$. We shall give a simple example that illustrates this. It shall also serve to illustrate our method.

Example 3.5.1 Let $H = I$, $B = I$, $A = 0$, $Q = \begin{bmatrix} 1 & 0 \\ 0 & 0 \end{bmatrix}$ be two by two matrices. The process is then simply $\dot{\underline{x}} = \underline{u}$, and cost is $\frac{1}{2}\int_{t_o}^{t_1} |x_1|^2 + |x_2|^2 + |u_1|^2 dt$, $\underline{x} = [x_1, x_2]^*$, $\underline{u} = [u_1, u_2]^*$. The system (4) becomes

$$\begin{bmatrix} I & 0 & 0 \\ 0 & I & 0 \\ 0 & 0 & 0 \end{bmatrix}\begin{bmatrix} \dot{\underline{\lambda}} \\ \dot{\underline{x}} \\ \dot{\underline{u}} \end{bmatrix} + \begin{bmatrix} 0 & I & 0 \\ 0 & 0 & -I \\ I & 0 & Q \end{bmatrix}\begin{bmatrix} \underline{\lambda} \\ \underline{x} \\ \underline{u} \end{bmatrix} = \begin{bmatrix} \underline{0} \\ \underline{0} \\ \underline{0} \end{bmatrix}. \quad (12)$$

Since $\mathcal{B}$ is invertible, we may take $\mu = 0$ in $(\mu\mathcal{A} + \mathcal{B})^{-1}$. Multiplying (4) by $\mathcal{B}^{-1} = \begin{bmatrix} 0 & Q & I \\ I & 0 & 0 \\ 0 & -I & 0 \end{bmatrix}$ gives

$$\begin{bmatrix} 0 & Q & 0 \\ I & 0 & 0 \\ 0 & -I & 0 \end{bmatrix}\begin{bmatrix} \dot{\underline{\lambda}} \\ \dot{\underline{x}} \\ \dot{\underline{u}} \end{bmatrix} + \begin{bmatrix} \underline{\lambda} \\ \underline{x} \\ \underline{u} \end{bmatrix} = \begin{bmatrix} \underline{0} \\ \underline{0} \\ \underline{0} \end{bmatrix}. \quad (13)$$

It is straightforward then to get that the solutions to (13) are given by

$$\begin{bmatrix} \underline{\lambda} \\ \underline{x} \\ \underline{u} \end{bmatrix} = e^{\begin{bmatrix} 0 & Q & 0 \\ Q & 0 & 0 \\ 0 & -Q & 0 \end{bmatrix} (t - t_o)} \begin{bmatrix} Q & 0 & 0 \\ 0 & Q & 0 \\ -Q & 0 & 0 \end{bmatrix} \begin{bmatrix} \underline{\lambda}_o \\ \underline{x}_o \\ \underline{u}_o \end{bmatrix} . \tag{14}$$

It is clear that for any $\underline{x}_o, \underline{x}_1$ there exists a control $\underline{u}$ sending $\underline{x}_o$ to $\underline{x}_1$. But the $\underline{x}$ in (14) only takes on values of the form $\begin{bmatrix} c \\ 0 \end{bmatrix}$ for scalar c. Thus in order for an optimal control to exist, $\underline{x}_o, \underline{x}_1$ must be of the form $\begin{bmatrix} c_o \\ 0 \end{bmatrix}, \begin{bmatrix} c_1 \\ 0 \end{bmatrix}$. A look at the power series for the exponential in (14) shows that (14) is

$$\begin{bmatrix} \underline{\lambda} \\ \underline{x} \\ \underline{u} \end{bmatrix} = \begin{bmatrix} \cosh(t-t_o)Q+(I-Q) & -\sinh(t-t_o)Q & 0 \\ -\sinh(t-t_o)Q & \cosh(t-t_o)Q+(I-Q) & 0 \\ -\cosh(t-t_o)Q+Q & -\sinh(t-t_o)Q & I \end{bmatrix} \begin{bmatrix} Q & 0 & 0 \\ 0 & Q & 0 \\ -Q & 0 & 0 \end{bmatrix} \begin{bmatrix} \underline{\lambda}_o \\ \underline{x}_o \\ \underline{u}_o \end{bmatrix}$$

$$= \begin{bmatrix} \cosh(t-t_o)Q & -\sinh(t-t_o)Q & 0 \\ -\sinh(t-t_o)Q & \cosh(t-t_o)Q & 0 \\ -\cosh(t-t_o)Q+Q & -\sinh(t-t_o)Q & 0 \end{bmatrix} \begin{bmatrix} \underline{\lambda}_o \\ \underline{x}_o \\ \underline{u}_o \end{bmatrix} .$$

If $\underline{x}_o = \begin{bmatrix} c_o \\ 0 \end{bmatrix}$ and $\underline{x}_1 = \begin{bmatrix} c_1 \\ 0 \end{bmatrix}$, we see that $t = t_o$ gives $\underline{u}_o = Q\underline{\lambda}_o$. Since

$\begin{bmatrix} \underline{\lambda}_o \\ \underline{x}_o \\ \underline{u}_o \end{bmatrix} \varepsilon\ \mathcal{R}\left(\begin{bmatrix} Q & 0 & 0 \\ 0 & Q & 0 \\ -Q & 0 & 0 \end{bmatrix}\right)$ we must have $\underline{\lambda}_o = \begin{bmatrix} \ell_o \\ 0 \end{bmatrix}$, and then $\underline{u}_o = \begin{bmatrix} -\ell_o \\ 0 \end{bmatrix}$.

Letting $t = t_1$ gives $c_1 = -\sinh(t_1 - t_o)\ell_o + \cosh(t_1 - t_o)c_o$. Solving for ℓ_o, we have

$$\underline{u} = \begin{bmatrix} \cosh(t-t_o)\{c_1 - \cosh(t_1-t_o)c_o\}/\sinh(t_1-t_o) \quad -\sinh(t-t_o)c_o \\ 0 \end{bmatrix}$$

as the optimal control. $\underline{x}$ can also be easily solved for if desired.

We have arrived then at the following procedure for solving the original problem. Given $\underline{x}_o, \underline{x}_1$ determine whether it is possible to go from $\underline{x}_o$ to $\underline{x}_1$ with an optimal control by solving (if possible) (11) for $\underline{\lambda}_o$ such that $\begin{bmatrix} \underline{\lambda}_o \\ \underline{x}_o \end{bmatrix} \varepsilon\ \mathcal{R}(N_\mu{}^D N_\mu)$. If $\underline{\lambda}_o$ is found, use the bottom half of (9) for $\underline{x}$ if $\underline{x}$ is needed. Use (9) and (10) to get the optimal control $\underline{u}$.

In working a given problem, it is sometimes simpler to solve (4) directly using the techniques used in deriving the formulas as done in this example, rather than try to use the formulas directly.

At this point, an obvious question is "What does Q_μ being invertible mean?" That is, "What is the physical significance of assuming the invertibility of Q_μ?" The answer itself is easily comprehended. The proof, however, requires some knowledge about Laplace transforms and analytic functions. The reader without such an understanding is encouraged to read the statement of the theorems. From (7) and (8) we have

$$Q_\mu = B_4 - B_3(\mu + B_1)^{-1}B_2 = Q - B^*(\mu + A^*)^{-1}H(\mu - A)^{-1}B. \tag{15}$$

If Q is invertible, then Q_μ is almost always invertible since $\lim_{\mu\to\infty} (\mu + A^*)^{-1} = 0$ and $\lim_{\mu\to\infty} (\mu - A)^{-1} = 0$. If Q is invertible, then it is obvious from (4) that $\underline{u}$ can be solved for in terms of $\underline{x}, \underline{\lambda}$. Theorem 3 shows that this can happen even when Q is not invertible.

We note without proof that

<u>Proposition 3.5.2</u> If F,G are positive semidefinite $r \times r$ matrices, then $F + G$ is invertible if and only if $\mathcal{N}(F) \cap \mathcal{N}(G) = \{\underline{0}\}$.

Of course, Q_μ is invertible almost always for real μ if and only if it is almost always invertible for complex μ. Let μ = is where s is real. Then

(14) becomes $Q_\mu = Q - B^*(is + A^*)^{-1}H(is - A)^{-1}B = Q + B^*(-is + A)^{-1*}H(-is + A)^{-1}B$. From Proposition 2 we have that Q_μ is invertible almost always if and only if

$\{\underline{0}\} = N(Q) \cap N(B^*(-is + A)^{-1*}H(-is + A)^{-1}B) = N(Q) \cap N(H^{1/2}(-is + A)^{-1}B) = N(Q) \cap N(H(-is + A)^{-1}B)$ for almost all real s. Thus we have proven that:

Theorem 3.5.4 Q_μ is invertible for almost all μ if and only if $N(Q) \cap N(H(-is + A)^{-1}B) = \{\underline{0}\}$ for almost every real s.

We need a technical result on analytic (1)-inverses before proceeding.

Theorem 3.5.5 Suppose that $A(\cdot)$ is an $m \times n$ matrix valued function such that $A_{ij}(z)$ is a fraction of polynomials for all i and j. Suppose also that $N(A(z))$ is nontrivial for all z in the domain of $A(\cdot)$. Then for any real number $\omega > 0$, there exists a $m \times n$ matrix valued function $B(\cdot)$ such that

(i) $B_{ij}(z)$ is a fraction of polynomials,

(ii) $R(B(z)) = N(A(z))$ for almost all z,

(iii) The poles of B are integral multiples of ωi, $\omega > 0$, are simple, and

(iv) $\|B(z)\| = O(1/|z|^3)$ as $|z| \to \infty$.

Proof Suppose that $A(\cdot)$ is an $m \times n$ matrix valued function such that $A_{ij}(z)$ is a fraction of polynomials for all i and j. Suppose also that $N(A(z))$ is nontrivial for all z in the domain of $A(\cdot)$. Let X be an $n \times m$ matrix of unknowns X_{ij}. Then $AXA = A$ is a consistent linear system of at most mn equations in mn unknowns. Denote this new system by $EZ = B$, $Z \in \mathbb{C}^{mn}$. Since the coefficients of $EZ = B$ are fractions of polynomials, there exists a real number K such that all minors of E are identically zero, or identically nonzero, for $|z| \geq K$. Thus $EZ = B$ can be solved by row operations (nonuniquely) to give a $F(\cdot)$ such that for $|z| \geq K$; $AFA = A$, the entries of $F(z)$ are fractions of polynomials in z, $\text{rank}(F(z))$ is constant, and $\text{rank}(F(z))$ is the maximum possible ($\dim N(A(z))$). Note that $(FA)_{ij}$ is a fraction of polynomials for all i and j. Let $z_1,\ldots,z_q$ be the poles of FA. Let $r_1,\ldots,r_q$ denote their multiplicities. Let r_o be such that $\|FA\| = O(|z|^{r_o})$ as $|z| \to \infty$. Set $a = r_o + r_1 + \ldots + r_q + 3$. Define

$$B(z) = \{ \prod_{j=1}^{q} (z - z_j)^{r_j} \prod_{p=1}^{a} (z - ip\omega)^{-1} \} (I - F(z)A(z)).$$

Then B clearly satisfies (i), (iii), and (iv). Since (ii) holds for $|z| \geq K$, it holds for almost all z by analytic continuation. □

We can now prove the following:

<u>Theorem 3.5.6</u> The following are equivalent:

(a) There exists an $\underline{x}_o, \underline{x}_1$ for which optimal controls exist, but are not unique.

(b) There is a trajectory from zero to zero of zero cost with nonzero control.

(c) Q_μ is not invertible for all μ.

<u>Proof</u> Clearly (b) ⇒ (a) since $J[\underline{0},\underline{0}] = 0$. To see that (a) ⇒ (b), let $(\underline{x},\underline{u})$, $(\hat{\underline{x}},\hat{\underline{u}})$ be two optimal solutions from $\underline{x}_o$ to $\underline{x}_1$. Then there exists $\underline{\lambda},\hat{\underline{\lambda}}$ so that $(\underline{\lambda},\underline{x},\underline{u})$ and $(\hat{\underline{\lambda}},\hat{\underline{x}},\hat{\underline{u}})$ satisfy (3). Thus $(\underline{\lambda} - \hat{\underline{\lambda}}, \underline{x} - \hat{\underline{x}}, \underline{u} - \hat{\underline{u}})$ satisfies (3) and hence is optimal by Theorem 1. But $(\underline{x} - \hat{\underline{x}})(t_o) = (\underline{x} - \hat{\underline{x}})(t_1) = \underline{0}$ and $\underline{u} - \hat{\underline{u}}$ is not identically zero. That $J[\underline{x} - \hat{\underline{x}}, \underline{u} - \hat{\underline{u}}] = 0$ follows from (5).

Suppose now that (b) holds so that there exists $\underline{x},\underline{u}$ such that $J[\underline{x},\underline{u}] = 0$, $\underline{x}(t_o) = \underline{0}$, $\underline{x}(t_1) = \underline{0}$, and $\underline{u}$ is nonzero. Since $J[\underline{x},\underline{u}] = 0$ it is clear from (2) that $H\underline{x} = \underline{0}$ and $Q\underline{u} = \underline{0}$. Extend $\underline{x},\underline{u}$ periodically to $[-\infty,\infty]$ and replace t by $t - t_o$. Call the new functions $\tilde{\underline{x}},\tilde{\underline{u}}$. Thus $H\tilde{\underline{x}} = \underline{0}$, $Q\tilde{\underline{u}} = \underline{0}$, and $\dot{\tilde{\underline{x}}} = A\tilde{\underline{x}} + B\tilde{\underline{u}}$, $t \neq n(t_1 - t_o)$, $n = 0,\pm1,\pm2,\ldots$. Since $\tilde{\underline{u}}$ is bounded and sectionally continuous on finite intervals, $\tilde{\underline{x}}$ is continuous, and $\tilde{\underline{x}}$ is of exponential order, we can take Laplace transforms to get $H\mathcal{L}[\tilde{\underline{x}}] = \underline{0}$, $Q\mathcal{L}[\tilde{\underline{u}}] = \underline{0}$, and $\mathcal{L}[\tilde{\underline{x}}] = (s - A)^{-1}B\mathcal{L}[\tilde{\underline{u}}]$. Thus $\mathcal{L}[\tilde{\underline{u}}](s) \in \mathcal{N}(Q) \cap \mathcal{N}(H(s - A)^{-1}B)$ for all s in some right half plane. By Theorem 4, we have Q_μ is not invertible for all μ.

Conversely, suppose that Q_μ is not invertible for all μ. From the proof of Theorem 4 we have $\mathcal{N}(Q) \cap \mathcal{N}(H(\mu - A)^{-1}B) = \mathcal{N}(Q_\mu)$ for $\mu = it$, t real. Thus $\mathcal{N}(Q) \cap \mathcal{N}(H(\mu - A)^{-1}B) = \mathcal{N}(Q_\mu)$ for almost all μ. Now applying Theorem 5 to Q_μ with $\omega = 2\pi/(t_1 - t_o)$ yields a B_μ such that $Q_\mu B_\mu = 0$, and B_μ satisfies (iii), (iv). But then $QB_\mu = 0$, and $H(\mu - A)^{-1}BB_\mu = 0$. Let $\underline{\phi}$ be vector such that $B_\mu\underline{\phi}$ is not identically zero. Denote $B_\mu\underline{\phi}$ by $\underline{\phi}(\mu)$. Let $\tilde{\underline{x}}(s) = (s - A)^{-1}B\underline{\phi}(s)$. Then we have that

$$H\tilde{\underline{x}}(s) = \underline{0},\ Q\underline{\phi}(s) = \underline{0},\ \text{and } \tilde{\underline{x}}(s) = (s - A)^{-1}B\underline{\phi}(s). \tag{16}$$

Let $\underline{x}$ be the inverse Laplace transform of $\tilde{\underline{x}}$, $\underline{u}$ the inverse Laplace transform of $\underline{\phi}$. From (16) and (iv) we have $H\hat{\underline{x}} = \underline{0}$, $Q\hat{\underline{\mu}} = \underline{0}$, $\dot{\underline{x}} = A\hat{\underline{x}} + B\hat{\underline{u}}$, $\hat{\underline{x}}(0) = \underline{0}$, and $\hat{\underline{u}}(0) = \underline{0}$. Furthermore, $\hat{\underline{u}}$ is nonzero. Finally, since the poles of $\underline{\phi}(s)$ were simple and multiples of $2\pi i/(t_1 - t_o)$ we get that $\hat{\underline{x}},\hat{\underline{u}}$ are periodic with period $(t_1 - t_o)$. [20, p. 188]. Replace $\hat{\underline{x}},\hat{\underline{u}}$ by $\underline{x} = \hat{\underline{x}}(t + t_o)$, $\underline{u} = \hat{\underline{u}}(t + t_o)$. Then $\underline{x}(t_o) = \underline{x}(t_1) = \underline{0}$, $J[\underline{x},\underline{u}] = 0$, and $\dot{\underline{x}} = A\underline{x} + B\underline{u}$. Thus (c) ⇒ (b). □

It is possible to have Q_μ invertible almost always and still have nonzero optimal trajectories of zero cost. Of course, the control $\underline{u}$ must then be zero.

Example 3.5.2 Let Q = I, A = I, B = 0, H = 0 in (2) and (3). Then Q_μ is invertible for large μ since Q is. Clearly $\underline{x} = \exp(A(t - t_o))\underline{x}_o$ is a trajectory of zero cost from $\underline{x}_o$ to $\underline{x}_1 = \exp(A(t_1 - t_o))\underline{x}_o$. But $\underline{u} = \underline{0}$ and $J[\underline{x},\underline{u}] = 0$. Note also if $\underline{x}_o = \underline{0}$, then $\underline{x} \equiv \underline{0}$.

We will make no use of "controllability," and hence will not define it. For the benefit of the reader familiar with the concept, note that the invertibility of Q_μ is logically independent of the controllability of (2) since for any choice of A,B, setting Q = I makes Q_μ invertible almost always, while setting Q = H = 0 makes $Q_\mu \equiv 0$.

Note also that in Example 2, the pair (A,B) was completely controllable and Q_μ was invertible. However, optimal controls only existed for certain pairs $\underline{x}_o,\underline{x}_1$. Thus the assumption of controllability does not seem to simplify matters if Q,H are allowed to be singular.

The method of this section can be applied, of course, to any problem which leads to a system of the form (1). However, the block lower triangularity of $\mathcal{A}$ made the computation of $\underline{u}$ from $\underline{x},\underline{\lambda}$ possible. Any problem which leads to a system of the form $\mathcal{A}\dot{\underline{z}} + \mathcal{B}\underline{z} = \underline{f}$ with $\mathcal{A} = \begin{bmatrix} A_1 & 0 \\ A_2 & 0 \end{bmatrix}$ can be solved much as was (6), provided, of course, $\mu\mathcal{A} + \mathcal{B}$ is invertible for some μ.

For example, suppose that the cost is given by $\int_{t_o}^{t_1} (H\underline{x},\underline{x}) + (Q\underline{u},\underline{u}) + (\underline{x},\underline{a})dt$ where $\underline{a} \in \mathbb{R}^n$. Then the right hand side of (4) has $\underline{\alpha} = [\underline{a}^*,\underline{0}^*,\underline{0}^*]^*$ instead of the zero vector.

Theorem 1.3 can be used to solve this nonhomogeneous system to get

$$\Omega = A^D e^{-\hat{A}^D\hat{B}t} \int_{t_o}^{t} e^{\hat{A}^D\hat{B}s}\hat{\underline{a}}ds + (I - \tilde{A}\tilde{A}^D)\hat{B}^D\hat{\underline{\alpha}} + e^{-\hat{A}^D\hat{B}t}\hat{A}^D\hat{A}\underline{q}.$$

The integral can be evaluated by using Theorem 1.4. For this problem, it is important to know whether or not the cost is positive.

6. DISCRETE SYSTEMS AND APPLICATIONS

This section will consider the discrete analogue of $A\dot{\underline{x}} = B\underline{x} + \underline{f}$, $A\underline{x}_{n+1} = B\underline{x}_n = \underline{f}_n$. First we shall develop the basic theory. These results will then be applied to the Discrete Control Problem of Section 2.2 and the Leontief Model of Section 2.5. Throughout this section n is an integer valued variable and the matrices A,B are m × m. Not unexpectedly the solution of the difference equation proceeds much as for the differential equation.

Definition 3.6.1 For $A,B \in \mathbb{C}^{m\times m}$, $\underline{f}_n \in \mathbb{C}^m$, the vector $\underline{c} \in \mathbb{C}^m$ is called a consistent initial vector for the difference equation $A\underline{x}_{n+1} = B\underline{x}_n + \underline{f}_n$ if the initial value problem $A\underline{x}_{n+1} = B\underline{x}_n + \underline{f}_n$, $\underline{x}_o = \underline{c}$, n = 1,2,... has a solution $\{\underline{x}_n\}$. The difference equation $A\underline{x}_{n+1} = B\underline{x}_n + \underline{f}_n$ is said to be tractable if the initial value problem $A\underline{x}_{n+1} = B\underline{x}_n + \underline{f}_n$, $x_o = \underline{c}$, n = 1,2,... has a unique solution for each consistent initial vector $\underline{c}$.

Theorem 3.6.1 The homogeneous difference equation $A\underline{x}_{n+1} = B\underline{x}_n$ $A,B \in \mathbb{C}^{m\times m}$ is tractable if and only if there exists a scalar $\lambda \in \mathbb{C}$ such that $(\lambda A + B)^{-1}$ exists.

The proof follows the same lines as the proof of Theorem 1.2 except that $\underline{x}_{\lambda_i}(t) = e^{\lambda_i t}\underline{v}_{\lambda_i}$ is replaced with $\underline{x}_n(\lambda_i) = \lambda_i^n\underline{v}_{\lambda_i}$. The difference analogue of Theorem 1.3 is

Theorem 3.6.2 If the homogeneous equation

$$A\underline{x}_{n+1} = B\underline{x}_n \tag{1}$$

is tractable, then the general solution is given by

$$\underline{x}_n = \begin{cases} \hat{A}\hat{A}^D\underline{q} & \text{if } n = 0, \\ (\hat{A}^D\hat{B})^n\underline{q} & \text{if } n \geq 1, \end{cases} \qquad \underline{q} \in \mathbb{C}^m$$

where $\hat{A} = (\lambda A - B)^{-1}A$ and $\hat{B} = (\lambda A - B)^{-1}B$ and $\lambda \in \mathbb{C}$ is such that $(\lambda A - B)^{-1}$ exists. Furthermore, $\underline{c} \in \mathbb{C}^m$ is a consistent initial vector for (1) if and only if $\underline{c} \in R(\hat{A}^k)$, where $k = \text{Ind}(\hat{A})$. In this case the unique solution, subject to $\underline{x}_0 = \underline{c}$, is given by $\underline{x}_n = (\hat{A}^D\hat{B})^n\underline{c}$, $n \geq 0$. The inhomogeneous equation $A\underline{x}_{n+1} = B\underline{x}_n + \underline{f}_n$ is also tractable. Its general solution is, for $n \geq 1$,

$$\underline{x}_n = (\hat{A}^D\hat{B})^n\hat{A}\hat{A}^D\underline{q} + \hat{A}^D\sum_{i=0}^{n-1}(\hat{A}^D\hat{B})^{n-i-1}\hat{\underline{f}}_i - (I-\hat{A}\hat{A}^D)\sum_{i=0}^{k-1}(\hat{A}\hat{B}^D)^i\hat{B}^D\hat{\underline{f}}_{n+i}, \tag{2}$$

where $\hat{\underline{f}}_i = (\lambda A - B)^{-1}\underline{f}_i$, $k = \text{Ind}(\hat{A})$, and $\underline{q} \in \mathbb{C}^m$. The solution $\underline{x}_n$ is independent of λ. Let $\hat{\underline{w}} = -(I - \hat{A}\hat{A}^D)\sum_{i=0}^{k-1}(\hat{A}\hat{B}^D)^i\hat{B}^D\hat{\underline{f}}_i$. The vector $\underline{c}$ is a consistent initial vector if and only if $\underline{c}$ lies in the set $\{\hat{\underline{w}} + R(\hat{A}^k)\}$.

Proof Since (1) is tractable, multiplying by $(\lambda A - B)^{-1}$ and performing a similarity gives, as in the proof of Theorem 2.1,

$$\begin{bmatrix} C & 0 \\ 0 & N \end{bmatrix}\begin{bmatrix} \underline{x}_{n+1}^{(1)} \\ \underline{x}_{n+1}^{(2)} \end{bmatrix} = \begin{bmatrix} I + \lambda C & 0 \\ 0 & I + \lambda N \end{bmatrix}\begin{bmatrix} \underline{x}_n^{(1)} \\ \underline{x}_n^{(2)} \end{bmatrix}. \tag{3}$$

Thus $\underline{x}_n^{(2)} = (I + \lambda N)^{-k} N^k \underline{x}_{n+k}^{(2)} = \underline{0}$, $\underline{x}_n^{(1)} = C^{-n}(I + \lambda C)^n \underline{x}_o^{(1)}$, and the solution of the homogeneous equation follows. (2) may also be verified directly as in the proof of Theorem 1.3. □

It is interesting to note that the solution (2) for $\underline{x}_n$ depends not only on the n + 1 vectors $\hat{\underline{f}}_o, \hat{\underline{f}}_1, \ldots, \hat{\underline{f}}_n$, but also on k - 1 "future" vectors $\hat{\underline{f}}_{n+1}, \hat{\underline{f}}_{n+2}, \ldots, \hat{\underline{f}}_{n+k-1}$. When A is nonsingular,

$\underline{x}_n = (A^{-1}B)^n \underline{q} + \sum_{i=0}^{n-1} (A^{-1}B)^{n-i-1} A^{-1} \underline{f}_i$ and $\underline{x}_n$ depends only on the past vectors $\underline{f}_o, \underline{f}_1, \ldots, \underline{f}_{n-1}$.

In many applications one has a difference equation holding for only a subset of the $\underline{x}_i$.

Theorem 3.6.3 Suppose that A,B are square matrices and there exists a scalar λ such that $\lambda A + B$ is nonsingular. Set $\hat{A} = (\lambda A + B)^{-1}A$ and $\hat{B} = (\lambda A + B)^{-1}B$, $\hat{\underline{f}} = (\lambda A + B)^{-1}\underline{f}$. Then all solutions of $A\underline{x}_{i+1} + B\underline{x}_i = \underline{f}_i$, $i = 0,\ldots,N - 1$ are given by

$$\hat{A}^D\hat{A}\underline{x}_i = (-\hat{A}^D\hat{B})^i \hat{A}^D\hat{A}\underline{x}_o + \sum_{\ell=0}^{i-1} (-\hat{A}^D\hat{B})^{\ell} \hat{A}^D \underline{f}_{i-\ell-1}, \text{ and}$$

$$(I - \hat{A}^D\hat{A})\underline{x}_i = (-\hat{A}\hat{B}^D)^{N-i}(I - \hat{A}^D\hat{A})\underline{x}_N + \sum_{\ell=0}^{N-i-1} (-\hat{A}\hat{B}^D)^{\ell}\hat{B}^D\underline{f}_{i+\ell}. \tag{4}$$

Proof Suppose there exists a λ such that $\lambda A + B$ is nonsingular. Taking a similarity we get, as in (3), $\hat{A} = \begin{bmatrix} A_1 & 0 \\ 0 & M \end{bmatrix}$, $\hat{B} = \begin{bmatrix} B_1 & 0 \\ 0 & B_2 \end{bmatrix}$, $\underline{x}_i = \begin{bmatrix} \underline{w}_i \\ \underline{v}_i \end{bmatrix}$, $\hat{\underline{f}}_i = \begin{bmatrix} \underline{g}_i \\ \underline{h}_i \end{bmatrix}$, with $B_1 = I - \lambda A_1$, $B_2 = I - \lambda M$, $M^k = 0$. Then the difference equation is equivalent to the decoupled equations $A_1\underline{w}_{i+1} + B_1\underline{w}_i = \underline{g}_i$, $M\underline{v}_{i+1} + B_2\underline{v}_i = \underline{h}_i$, $i = 0,\ldots,N - 1$. Since A_1, B_2 are invertible, we get $\underline{w}_{i+1} = A_1^{-1}\underline{g}_i - A_1^{-1}B_1\underline{w}_i$, and $\underline{v}_i = B_2^{-1}\underline{h}_i - B_2^{-1}M\underline{v}_{i+1}$. Thus

$$\underline{w}_i = (-A_1^{-1}B_1)^i \underline{w}_o + \sum_{\ell=0}^{i-1} (-A_1^{-1}B_1)^{\ell} A_1^{-1} \underline{g}_{i-\ell-1},$$

$$\underline{v}_i = (-B_2^{-1}M)^{N-i} \underline{v}_N + \sum_{\ell=0}^{N-i-1} (-B_2^{-1}M)^{\ell} B_2^{-1} \underline{h}_{i+\ell}.$$ (4) now follows. □

Discrete control problem

As an application of Theorem 2 consider the Discrete Control Problem of Section 2.2. Recall that N was fixed, the process was $\underline{x}_{i+1} = A\underline{x}_i + B\underline{u}_i$, $i = 0,\ldots,N-1$, $\underline{x}_o$ was specified, and the cost was given by $J[\underline{x},\underline{u}] = \frac{1}{2} \sum_{i=0}^{N} (H\underline{x}_i,\underline{x}_i) + (Q\underline{u}_i,\underline{u}_i)$. Note that the terminal position is not specified whereas it was in the continuous problem considered in Section 5.

Theorem 3.6.4 The Discrete Control Problem has a solution $\{\underline{x}_i\}$, $\{\underline{u}_i\}$, if and only if there exists $\{\underline{\lambda}_i\}$ such that the sequences $\{\underline{x}_i\}$, $\{\underline{\lambda}_i\}$, $\{\underline{u}_i\}$ satisfy

$$\begin{bmatrix} I & 0 & 0 \\ H & -A^* & 0 \\ 0 & 0 & 0 \end{bmatrix} \begin{bmatrix} \underline{x}_{i+1} \\ \underline{\lambda}_{i+1} \\ \underline{u}_{i+1} \end{bmatrix} + \begin{bmatrix} -A & 0 & -B \\ 0 & I & 0 \\ 0 & -B^* & Q \end{bmatrix} \begin{bmatrix} \underline{x}_i \\ \underline{\lambda}_i \\ \underline{u}_i \end{bmatrix} = \begin{bmatrix} \underline{0} \\ \underline{0} \\ \underline{0} \end{bmatrix} \tag{5}$$

for $i = 0,1,\ldots,N-1$, with $\underline{x}_o$ given and $\underline{\lambda}_N = \underline{0}$, $\underline{u}_N = \underline{0}$.

Proof Since $\underline{u}_N$ only appears in the cost and does not effect the $\{\underline{x}_i\}$, $\underline{u}_N$ may be taken to be any vector such that $Q\underline{u}_N = \underline{0}$. Take $\underline{u}_N = \underline{0}$. To see the necessity of (5) consider $J[\underline{x},\underline{u}] + \sum_{i=0}^{N-1} (\underline{\lambda}_i, \underline{x}_{i+1} - A\underline{x}_i - B\underline{u}_i)$ and set $\underline{\lambda}_N = \underline{0}$.

Then $\dfrac{\partial(\underline{x}_1 - A\underline{x}_o - B\underline{u}_o,\ldots,\underline{x}_N - A\underline{x}_{N-1} - B\underline{u}_{N-1})}{\partial(\underline{x}_1,\ldots,\underline{x}_n)} = 1$ where $(\underline{z}_1,\ldots,\underline{z}_n)$ is to be considered as a list of the n entries of $\underline{z}_1$, then the n entries of $\underline{z}_2$, etc. Thus one gets by the usual theory of Lagrange multipliers that

$$\begin{aligned}
&H\underline{x}_i - A^*\underline{\lambda}_i + \underline{\lambda}_{i-1} = \underline{0}, \quad i = 1,\ldots,N-1,\\
&H\underline{x}_N + \underline{\lambda}_{N-1} = \underline{0},\\
&Q\underline{u}_i - B^*\underline{\lambda}_i = \underline{0}, \qquad i = 0,\ldots,N-1\\
&\underline{x}_{i+1} - A\underline{x}_i - B\underline{u}_i = \underline{0}, \quad i = 0,\ldots,N-1
\end{aligned} \tag{6}$$

is necessary. But (6) is equivalent to (5) since $\underline{\lambda}_N$ was taken equal to zero. On the other hand if $\{\underline{x}_i\}$, $\{\underline{u}_i\}$, $\{\underline{\lambda}_i\}$ satisfy (6), then one may show, almost exactly as for Theorem 5.1, that $J[s\underline{x} + (1 - s)\hat{\underline{x}}, s\underline{u} + (1 - s)\hat{\underline{u}}]$, $\hat{\underline{x}}_{i+1} = A\hat{\underline{x}}_i + B\hat{\underline{u}}_i$, $i = 0,\ldots,N - 1$, has a minimum at $s = 1$. We omit the details. □

Unlike the continuous problem of Section 5, the control problem considered here can have arbitrary $\underline{x}_o$.

<u>Theorem 3.6.5</u> Suppose that $Q + B^*(-\mu A^* + I)^{-1}\mu H(\mu - A)^{-1}B$ is invertible for some scalar μ (and hence for all but a finite number of μ). Then for every $\underline{x}_o$ there exists a solution to the Discrete Control Problem.

<u>Proof</u> Given $\underline{x}_o$, $J[\underline{x},\underline{u}]$ defines a C^∞ function on $\mathbb{R}^{Nm}$. Since J is bounded below, it suffices to show that $J[\underline{x},\underline{u}]$ goes to infinity as $\sum_{i=0}^{N} \|\underline{u}_i\|^2$ does. If Q is invertible, this is clear. Suppose then that Q is singular and $Q + B^*(-\mu A^* + I)^{-1}\mu H(\mu - A)^{-1}B = Q_\mu$ is nonsingular for almost all μ. Suppose for purposes of contradiction that there exists a sequence of control sequences $\{\underline{u}_{ir}\}$, $i = 0,\ldots,N - 1$; $r = 0,\ldots,$ such that $\sum_{i=0}^{N-1} \|\underline{u}_{ir}\|^2 \to \infty$ but $J[\underline{x}_r,\underline{u}_r]$ is bounded.

We shall show that, in fact, $\{\underline{u}_{ir}\}$ is bounded as $r \to \infty$. Since $J[\underline{x}_r,\underline{u}_r]$ is bounded, one has $(Q\underline{u}_{or},\underline{u}_{or})$ is bounded. Hence $Q^{1/2}\underline{u}_{or}$ is bounded. But $(H\underline{x}_{1r},\underline{x}_{1r}) = \|H^{1/2}(A\underline{x}_{or} + B\underline{u}_{or})\|^2$ is also bounded. Then $H^{1/2}B\underline{u}_{or}$ is bounded since $\underline{x}_{or} = \underline{x}_o$ for all r. But Q_μ is invertible for almost all μ, so that $\underline{u}_{or}$ is bounded. Hence $\underline{x}_{1r}$ is bounded. Proceeding in this manner, one gets $\sum_{i=0}^{N-1} \|\underline{u}_{ir}\|^2$ is bounded. Thus J attains its minimum as desired. □

We can now solve the Discrete Control Problem. Let $A_1 = \begin{bmatrix} I & 0 \\ H & -A \end{bmatrix}$, $B_1 = \begin{bmatrix} -A & 0 \\ 0 & I \end{bmatrix}$, $B_2 = \begin{bmatrix} -B \\ 0 \end{bmatrix}$, $B_3 = \begin{bmatrix} 0 & -B^* \end{bmatrix}$, $B_4 = Q$ and $\underline{z}_i = \begin{bmatrix} \underline{x}_i \\ \underline{\lambda}_i \end{bmatrix}$. Then (5) becomes $\begin{bmatrix} A_1 & 0 \\ 0 & 0 \end{bmatrix} \begin{bmatrix} \underline{z}_{i+1} \\ \underline{u}_{i+1} \end{bmatrix} + \begin{bmatrix} B_1 & B_2 \\ B_3 & B_4 \end{bmatrix} \begin{bmatrix} \underline{z}_i \\ \underline{u}_i \end{bmatrix} = \begin{bmatrix} \underline{0} \\ \underline{0} \end{bmatrix}$, $0 \le i \le N-1$.

<u>Proposition 3.6.1</u> Let $Q_\mu = B_4 - B_3 H_\mu^{-1} B_2 = Q + B^*(\mu A^* + I)^{-1} H(\mu - A)^{-1} B$ where μ is such $\mu A^* + I$ and $\mu - A$ are invertible. Then

$$\begin{bmatrix} \mu A_1 + B_1 & B_2 \\ B_2 & B_4 \end{bmatrix}$$

is invertible if and only if Q_μ is invertible.

It is assumed from here on that (7) and $\mu A_1 + B_1$ are invertible. Multiply (5) by the inverse of (7) to get

$$\begin{bmatrix} N_\mu & 0 \\ M_\mu & 0 \end{bmatrix} \begin{bmatrix} \underline{z}_{i+1} \\ \underline{u}_{i+1} \end{bmatrix} + \begin{bmatrix} Z_\mu & 0 \\ -\mu M_\mu & I \end{bmatrix} \begin{bmatrix} \underline{z}_i \\ \underline{u}_i \end{bmatrix} = \begin{bmatrix} \underline{0} \\ \underline{0} \end{bmatrix}, \tag{8}$$

with $\underline{u}_N = \underline{0}$, $\underline{\lambda}_N = \underline{0}$, $\underline{x}_o$ given, $\mu N_\mu + Z_\mu = I$. But

$$\begin{bmatrix} N_\mu & 0 \\ M_\mu & 0 \end{bmatrix}^D = \begin{bmatrix} N_\mu^D & 0 \\ M_\mu N_\mu^{D^2} & 0 \end{bmatrix}, \text{ and } \begin{bmatrix} Z_\mu & 0 \\ W_\mu & I \end{bmatrix}^D = \begin{bmatrix} Z_\mu^D & 0 \\ L_\mu & I \end{bmatrix}.$$

Here $L_\mu = (W_\mu + W_\mu Z_\mu + \ldots + W_\mu Z_\mu^{\ell-1})(I - Z_\mu^D Z_\mu) - W_\mu Z_\mu^D$, $\ell = \text{Ind}(Z_\mu)$.

By Theorem 3, all solutions of (8) are given by

$$\begin{bmatrix} \underline{z}_i \\ \underline{u}_i \end{bmatrix} = \begin{bmatrix} -N_\mu^D Z_\mu & 0 \\ -M_\mu N_\mu^{D^2} Z_\mu & 0 \end{bmatrix}^i \begin{bmatrix} N_\mu^D N_\mu & 0 \\ M_\mu N_\mu^D & 0 \end{bmatrix} \begin{bmatrix} \underline{z}_o \\ \underline{u}_o \end{bmatrix}$$

$$+ \begin{bmatrix} -Z_\mu^D N_\mu & 0 \\ -(L_\mu N_\mu + M_\mu) & 0 \end{bmatrix}^{N-i} \begin{bmatrix} I - N_\mu^D N_\mu & 0 \\ -M_\mu N_\mu^D & I \end{bmatrix} \begin{bmatrix} \underline{z}_N \\ \underline{0} \end{bmatrix}.$$

A solution (9) will satisfy the boundary conditions if and only if

$$\underline{z}_o = N_\mu^D N_\mu \underline{z}_o + (-Z_\mu^D N_\mu)^N (I - N_\mu^D N_\mu) \underline{z}_N, \tag{10}$$

$$\underline{u}_o = M_\mu N_\mu^D \underline{z}_o = (L_\mu N_\mu + M_\mu)(-Z_\mu^D N_\mu)^{N-1} (I - N_\mu^D M_\mu) \underline{z}_N, \tag{11}$$

$$\underline{z}_N = (-N_\mu^D Z_\mu)^N N_\mu^D N_\mu \underline{z}_o + (I - N_\mu^D N_\mu) \underline{z}_N, \tag{12}$$

and

$$\underline{0} = M_\mu (N_\mu^D)^2 Z_\mu (-N_\mu^D Z_\mu)^{N-1} N_\mu^D N_\mu \underline{z}_o - M_\mu N_\mu^D \underline{z}_N. \tag{13}$$

Recall that $\mu N_\mu + Z_\mu = I$. Thus N_μ^D and Z_μ commute. Using (12), (13) becomes $-M_\mu(-N_\mu^D)^{N+1} Z_\mu^N N_\mu^D N_\mu \underline{z}_o - M_\mu N_\mu^D (-N_\mu^D Z_\mu)^N N_\mu^D N_\mu \underline{z}_o = \underline{0}$. The preceding discussion is summarized in the following theorem.

Theorem 3.6.6 Suppose that Q_μ is invertible, that $N > \mathrm{Ind}(N_\mu)$, and $\underline{x}_o$ is specified. Then $\underline{\lambda}_o$, $\underline{x}_n$ are gotten by solving

$$(I - N_\mu^D N_\mu) \begin{bmatrix} \underline{x}_o \\ \underline{\lambda}_o \end{bmatrix} = \underline{0}, \text{ and } N_\mu^D N_\mu \begin{bmatrix} \underline{x}_N \\ \underline{0} \end{bmatrix} = (-N_\mu^D Z_\mu)^N \begin{bmatrix} \underline{x}_o \\ \underline{\lambda}_o \end{bmatrix}.$$

The control sequence is given by $\underline{u} = M_\mu N_\mu^D \begin{bmatrix} \underline{x}_o \\ \underline{\lambda}_o \end{bmatrix}$, and for i > 0 by,

$$\underline{u}_i = M_\mu N_\mu^D Z_\mu (-N_\mu^D Z_\mu)^i \begin{bmatrix} \underline{x}_o \\ \underline{\lambda}_o \end{bmatrix} - (L_\mu N_\mu + M_\mu)(-Z_\mu^D N_\mu)^{N-i-1}(I - N_\mu^D N_\mu) \begin{bmatrix} \underline{x}_N \\ \underline{0} \end{bmatrix}.$$

As mentioned earlier, one is probably better off to follow the steps in the proof of Theorem 6 rather than try to utilize the formulas.

If the process is not completely controllable, and $\underline{x}_o$ is a point that cannot be steered to the origin, then $\underline{x}_N$ will be unequal to zero. A very simple example is gotten by taking A = I, B = 0, and Q invertible. Then Q_μ is invertible. In this case, of course, one would get $\underline{x}_i = \underline{x}_o$, and $\underline{u}_i = \underline{0}$ for all i.

It is possible to have Q not invertible, the process not completely controllable and Q_μ still be invertible and our results apply. One may take $A = 0$, $B = H = \begin{bmatrix} 1 & 0 \\ 0 & 0 \end{bmatrix}$ and $Q = \begin{bmatrix} 0 & 0 \\ 0 & 1 \end{bmatrix}$ for an example.

In applications it frequently happens that Q is invertible. Unlike the continuous control problem, the discrete problem can still give rise to a singular difference equation when Q is invertible.

If Q in the Discrete Control Problem is nonsingular, then $\underline{u}_i = Q^{-1}B^*\underline{\lambda}_i$ for i = 0,1,...,N - 1 and (5) becomes

$$\mathcal{A}\underline{z}_{i+1} + \mathcal{B}\underline{z}_i = \begin{bmatrix} I & 0 \\ H & -A^* \end{bmatrix} \begin{bmatrix} \underline{x}_{i+1} \\ \underline{\lambda}_{i+1} \end{bmatrix} + \begin{bmatrix} -A & -BQ^{-1}B^* \\ 0 & I \end{bmatrix} \begin{bmatrix} \underline{x}_i \\ \underline{\lambda}_i \end{bmatrix} = \begin{bmatrix} \underline{0} \\ \underline{0} \end{bmatrix}, \quad (14)$$

for i = 0,1,...,N - 1, and $\underline{\lambda}_N = \underline{0}$.

$\mathcal{A}$ is invertible if and only if A is. However, there always exists a μ such that $\mu\mathcal{A} + \mathcal{B}$ is invertible so that Theorem 3 can always be applied. The The difference equation (14) has the advantage that one can work with matrices that are 2n × 2n instead of (2n + m) × (2n + m).

While $N \geq \mathrm{Ind}(\hat{A})$ was assumed in the statement of the theorems, the assumption is not really necessary. If $N < \mathrm{Ind}(\hat{A})$, one may still use Theorem 3 to solve (5).

The Leontief model

Recall from Section 2.5, that the Leontief model of a multisector economy can be written as $B\underline{x}_{i+1} = R\underline{x}_i - \underline{d}_i$, $i = 0,1,\ldots,N-1$. Applying Theorem 3 to this system gives:

Theorem 3.6.7 Suppose that $\lambda B + R$ is invertible for some λ. Let $\hat{B} = (\lambda B + R)^{-1}B$, $\hat{\underline{d}}_i = (\lambda B + R)^{-1}\underline{d}_i$. Then

$$\hat{B}^D\hat{B}\underline{x}_i = [\hat{B}^D(I - \lambda\hat{B})]^{i-1}\underline{x}_o + \sum_{\ell=0}^{i-1} [\hat{B}^D(I - \lambda\hat{B})]^{\ell}\hat{B}^D\hat{\underline{d}}_{i-\ell-1} \tag{15}$$

$$(I - \hat{B}^D\hat{B})\underline{x}_i = [(I - \lambda\hat{B})^D\hat{B}]^{N-i}(I - \hat{B}^D\hat{B})\underline{x}_N + (I - \lambda\hat{B})^D \sum_{\ell=0}^{N-i-1} [(I - \lambda\hat{B})^D\hat{B}]^{\ell}(I - \hat{B}^D\hat{B})\hat{\underline{d}}_{\ell+i} \tag{16}$$

Note that $\hat{B}^{\ell}(I - \hat{B}^D\hat{B}) = 0$ if $\ell \geq \mathrm{Ind}(\hat{B})$. Thus if the economy is more than $\mathrm{Ind}(B)$ time units from the terminal time N, in particular if the economy is assumed to run for all time, we get,

$$(I - \hat{B}^D\hat{B})\underline{x}_i = \sum_{\ell=0}^{k-1} [(I - \lambda\hat{B})^D]^{\ell+1}\hat{B}^{\ell}(I - \hat{B}^D\hat{B})\hat{\underline{d}}_{\ell+i}, \quad k = \mathrm{Ind}(\hat{B}). \tag{17}$$

That is, $(I - B^DB)\underline{x}_i$ is determined by part of the demand in the next $k - 1$ units of time. We note in passing that an analogous behavior is observed in backwards projection using the Leslie population model.

That $\underline{x}_i$ should depend on future demand is not as odd as it sounds. It is not totally unreasonable to imagine a situation where future demand can effect current output levels. This would be particularly true if because of, announced governmental policies, future demand levels were known.

Equation (17) shows an advantage of our approach. Previous methods for nonregular Leontief models required backwards iteration from $\underline{x}_N$. As (17) shows this need not be done. For models with N large, (15), (17) could represent a substantially easier method. Also, our method works equally well for infinite time periods, in which case it would be easy to do an asymptotic analysis of (15), (17). (See [2].)

Note also that from (15), (17), one gets an explicit characterization of what $\underline{x}_o$ is. If $N \geq \mathrm{Ind}(\hat{B})$, then $\underline{x}(0)$ must be of the form

$$\hat{B}^D\hat{B}\underline{b} + \sum_{i=0}^{k-1} [(I - \hat{B})^D]^{i+1}\hat{B}^i(I - \hat{B}^D\hat{B})\underline{\hat{d}}_i, \quad \underline{b} \text{ an arbitrary vector.}$$

We would now like to examine in a little more detail our assumption that $\lambda B + R$ is invertible. First we shall show it is weaker than the regularity of Luenberger. In [10] Luenberger multiplies the Leontief system on the left by an invertible matrix P (does elementary row operations) to get

$$\begin{bmatrix} T \\ 0 \end{bmatrix} \underline{x}_{i+1} = \begin{bmatrix} G \\ H \end{bmatrix} \underline{x}_i - P\underline{d}_i, \tag{18}$$

where T has full row rank. He then shows (18) is regular if and only if $\begin{bmatrix} T \\ H \end{bmatrix}$ is nonsingular.

Note $P(\lambda B + R)$ is nonsingular if and only if $\lambda B + R$ is. Thus to show that regularity is stronger than our assumption it suffices to prove that

$$\text{If } \begin{bmatrix} T \\ H \end{bmatrix} \text{ is nonsingular, then } \begin{bmatrix} \lambda T + G \\ H \end{bmatrix} \text{ is nonsingular for some } \lambda. \tag{19}$$

Now $\begin{bmatrix} \lambda T + G \\ H \end{bmatrix}$ is nonsingular if and only if $\begin{bmatrix} 1/\lambda & 0 \\ 0 & I \end{bmatrix} \begin{bmatrix} \lambda T + G \\ H \end{bmatrix} = \begin{bmatrix} T + G/\lambda \\ H \end{bmatrix}$

is. But $\begin{bmatrix} T + G/\lambda \\ H \end{bmatrix} \to \begin{bmatrix} T \\ H \end{bmatrix}$ as $\lambda \to \infty$. Thus (19) follows since any matrix close enough to $\begin{bmatrix} T \\ H \end{bmatrix}$ must be nonsingular if $\begin{bmatrix} T \\ H \end{bmatrix}$ is.

Once it is known that our assumption is properly weaker than regularity, it is easy to characterize regularity. Since $\hat{B}(I - \hat{B}^D\hat{B}) = 0$ if and only if $\text{Ind}(\hat{B}) \leq 1$, we have immediately from Theorem 7,

<u>Proposition 3.6.2</u> The Leontief system will be regular in the sense of Luenberger if and only if there is a λ such that $\lambda B + R$ is invertible and $\text{Ind}(\hat{B}) \leq 1$.

7. <u>EXERCISES</u>

1. If $A\dot{\underline{x}} + B\underline{x} = \underline{0}$ is tractable and $A,B \in \mathbb{C}^{2\times 2}$ are singular, then the only solutions are constants.
2. If $(\lambda A + B)^{-1}$ exists for some λ, then
$$\hat{A}\hat{A}^D = \lim_{\lambda\to\infty} \frac{A_\lambda^D}{\lambda}, \quad \hat{A}^D\hat{B} = \lim_{\lambda\to 0} \hat{A}_\lambda^D.$$
3. If $\lambda A + B$ is one-to-one, and $N(\overline{\lambda}A^* + B^*) = N(A^*) \cap N(B^*)$, then all solutions of $A\dot{\underline{x}} + B\underline{x} = \underline{0}$ are of the form $\underline{x} = e^{-\hat{A}^D\hat{B}t}\hat{A}^D\hat{A}\underline{q}$ where $\underline{q}$ is an arbitrary vector.
4. Suppose $\lambda A + B$ is one-to-one and $N(\lambda A^* + B^*) = N(A^*) \cap N(B^*)$. Then $A\dot{\underline{x}} + B\underline{x} = \underline{f}$ is consistent if and only if $(I - (\lambda A + B)(\lambda A + B)^\dagger)\underline{f} = \underline{0}$.
5. Prove that if A,B are hermitian, then $(\lambda A + B)^\dagger A$, $(\lambda A + B)^\dagger B$ commute if and only if there exists a $\tilde{\lambda}$ such that $N(\tilde{\lambda}A + B) = N(A) \cap N(B)$. Furthermore, if $\tilde{\lambda}$ exists, then $(\tilde{\lambda}A + B)^\dagger A$, $(\tilde{\lambda}A + B)^\dagger B$ commute.
6. Prove that if $A,B \in \mathbb{C}^{n\times n}$ are such that one is EP, $(CC^\dagger = C^\dagger C)$ and the other is positive semidefinite, then there exists λ such that $\lambda A + B$ is invertible if and only if $N(A) \cap N(B) = \{\underline{0}\}$.

7. Suppose that $A,B \in \mathbb{C}^{n\times n}$ are such that $N(A) \cap N(B)$ reduces both A and B. Suppose also that there exists λ such that $N(\lambda A + B) = N(A) \cap N(B)$. Prove that then $A\dot{\underline{x}} + B\underline{x} = \underline{f}$, $\underline{f}$ n-times continuously differentiable, is consistent if and only if $\underline{f}(t) \in R(\lambda A + B)$ for all t, that is, $(\lambda A + B)(\lambda A + B)^{\dagger}\underline{f} = \underline{f}$. And that if it is consistent, then all solutions are of the form

$$\underline{x} = \hat{A}^D e^{-\hat{A}^D\hat{B}t}\int_0^t e^{\hat{A}^D\hat{B}s}\hat{\underline{f}}(s)ds$$

$$+ [(\lambda A + B)^D(\lambda A + B) - \hat{A}\hat{A}^D]\sum_{m=0}^{k-1}(-1)^m[\hat{A}\hat{B}^D]^m\hat{B}^D\hat{\underline{f}}^{(m)}$$

$$+ e^{-\hat{A}^D\hat{B}t}\hat{A}^D\hat{A}\underline{q} + [I - (\lambda A + B)^D(\lambda A + B)]\underline{g}$$

where $\hat{A} = (\lambda A + B)^D A$, $\hat{B} = (\lambda A + B)^D B$, $\hat{\underline{f}} = (\lambda A + B)^D\underline{f}$, $\underline{q}$ is an arbitrary vector, $\underline{g}$ an arbitrary vector valued function, and $k = \text{Ind}(\hat{A})$.

8. Prove that if A,B are EP ($CC^{\dagger} = C^{\dagger}C$) and one is positive semidefinite, then there exists a λ such that $N(\lambda A + B) = N(A) \cap N(B)$. Thus all solutions of $A\dot{\underline{x}} + B\underline{x} = \underline{f}$ are in the form given in Excercise 7.

9. Derive an expression for the consistent set of initial conditions for $A\dot{\underline{x}} + B\underline{x} = \underline{f}$ when $\underline{f}$ is n-times differentiable and $\lambda A + B$ is onto.

10. Solve $A\dot{\underline{x}}(t) + B\underline{x}(t) = \underline{b}$, A,B as in Example 1.5, $\underline{b} = [120]^*$.

Answer:
$$x_1(t) = -\frac{1}{18}e^{2/3t}(x_2(0) + 2x_3(0)) - \frac{13}{18}x_2(0) - \frac{4}{9}x_3(0) - \frac{2}{9} - t$$
$$x_2(t) = -\frac{4}{9}e^{2/3t}(x_2(0) + 2x_3(0)) - \frac{13}{9}x_2(0) + \frac{8}{9}x_3(0) + \frac{2}{9} + t$$
$$x_3(t) = \frac{13}{18}e^{2/3t}(x_2(0) + 2x_3(0)) - \frac{13}{18}x_2(0) - \frac{4}{3}x_3(0) - \frac{10}{9} - t$$

11. Let $d(\lambda) = \det(\lambda A + B)$. Prove that the dimension of the solution space of $A\dot{\underline{x}} + B\underline{x} = \underline{f}$ is the degree of $d(\lambda)$.

4 The Laplace transform

1. INTRODUCTION

In many disciplines the Laplace transform is widely used. In this chapter we shall show how

$$A\dot{\underline{x}} + B\underline{x} = \underline{f} \quad , \quad A,B \in \mathbb{C}^{n\times n} \tag{1}$$

can be solved using the Laplace transform. For a vector valued function $\underline{g}(t)$ let $L[\underline{g}] = \int_0^\infty e^{-st}\underline{g}(t)dt$ be the Laplace transform of $\underline{g}$. Applying L to (1) we get $sAL[\underline{x}] - A\underline{x}(0^+) + BL[\underline{x}] = L[\underline{f}]$, or $(sA + B)L[x] = L[\underline{f}] + A\underline{x}(0^+)$. If $sA + B$ is invertible for some s, then

$$L[\underline{x}] = (sA + B)^{-1}(L[\underline{f}] + A\underline{x}(0^+)). \tag{2}$$

To analyze (2) it is helpful to have an expansion of $(sA + B)^{-1}$. The next section will develop that expansion.

By utilizing some of the ideas of Section 2, much of this chapter can be extended to cover the case when $A,B \in \mathbb{C}^{m\times n}$ and $sA + B$ is either one-to-one or onto. That extension is left to the interested reader. This chapter is based on the work of Rose in [61].

2. EXPANSION OF $(sA + B)^{-1}$

For applications involving the Laplace transform we need the expansion of $(sA + B)^{-1}$ for large s. It turns out to be slightly easier to first expand $(A + \lambda B)^{-1}$ for λ near zero. If $A,B \in \mathbb{C}^{n\times n}$ and $A + \lambda B$ is invertible for some $\lambda \in \mathbb{C}$, then the elements of $(A + \lambda B)^{-1}$ are rational functions of λ. Thus, for some $r > 0$ and $0 < |\lambda| < r$, we have the Laurent expansion

$$(A + \lambda B)^{-1} = \sum_{k=-\nu}^{\infty} Q_k \lambda^k, \quad Q_{-\nu} \neq 0 \tag{1}$$

where the coefficient matrices $Q_k \in \mathbb{C}^{n\times n}$ are independent of λ and are uniquely determined by A and B. The nonnegative integer ν is also independent of λ and uniquely determined by A and B. If $\nu > 0$, then $(A + \lambda B)^{-1}$ has a pole of order ν at $\lambda = 0$. When $B = I$, $(A + \lambda I)^{-1}$, which always exists in a deleted neighborhood of $\lambda = 0$, is often called the resolvent of A. Thus $(A + \lambda B)^{-1}$ can be considered a generalized resolvent.

In [47] Langenhop has characterized the Q_k and ν, however explicit representations were not given. See also [35] for a similar development.

The main result of this section is

Theorem 4.2.1 Assume $A, B \in \mathbb{C}^{n\times n}$ and $(s_o A + B)^{-1}$ exists for $s_o \in \mathbb{C}$. Then $(sA + B)^{-1}$ exists for $|s| > R$ for some $R > 0$ and the following holds for $|s| > R$,

$$\begin{aligned}(sA + B)^{-1} = \{&\hat{A}^D \sum_{k=0}^{\infty} (-\hat{A}^D\hat{B})^k s^{-k-1} \\ &+ \hat{B}^D(I - \hat{A}\hat{A}^D) \sum_{k=0}^{\nu-1} (-\hat{A}\hat{B}^D)^k s^k\}(s_o A + B)^{-1}\end{aligned} \tag{2}$$

where $\hat{A} = (s_o A + B)^{-1}A$, $\hat{B} = (s_o A + B)^{-1}B$ and $\nu = \text{Ind}(\hat{A})$. (The second term of (2) is zero if $\nu = 0$.)

Proof Let $\lambda = 1/s$, and λ_o be such that $(A + \lambda_o B)^{-1}$ exists. Since $\hat{A}^D\hat{B}$, $\hat{A}\hat{B}^D$, $\hat{A}^D(s_o A + B)^{-1}$, $\hat{B}^D(s_o A + B)^{-1}$ and $\text{Ind}(\hat{A})$ are independent of s_o, to prove (2) it suffices to show that for small $|\lambda|$,

$$\begin{aligned}(A + \lambda B)^{-1} = \{&\hat{A}^D \sum_{k=0}^{\infty} (-1)^k (\hat{A}^D\hat{B})^k \lambda^k \\ &+ \hat{B}^D(I - \hat{A}\hat{A}^D) \sum_{k=0}^{\nu-1} (-1)^k (\hat{A}\hat{B}^D)^k \lambda^{k-1}\}(A + \lambda_o B)^{-1}\end{aligned} \tag{3}$$

where now $\hat{A} = (A + \lambda_o B)^{-1}A$, $\hat{B} = (A + \lambda_o B)^{-1}B$. As in Chapter 3, $\hat{A}$, $\hat{B}$, $\hat{A}^D$, $\hat{B}^D$ all compute. Multiplying (3) on the right by $(A + \lambda_o B)$ gives

$$(\hat{A}+\lambda\hat{B})^{-1} = \hat{A}^D \sum_{k=0}^{\infty} (-1)^k(\hat{A}^D\hat{B})^k\lambda^k + \hat{B}^D(I-\hat{A}\hat{A}^D) \sum_{k=0}^{\nu-1} (-1)^k(\hat{A}\hat{B}^D)^k\lambda^{-k-1}. \quad (4)$$

To prove (4), note that

$$(\hat{A} + \lambda\hat{B})^{-1} = (\hat{A} + \lambda\hat{B})^{-1}\hat{A}\hat{A}^D + (\hat{A} + \lambda\hat{B})^{-1}(I - \hat{A}\hat{A}^D) \quad (5)$$

$$= \hat{A}^D(I + \lambda\hat{A}^D\hat{B})^{-1} + \lambda^{-1}\hat{B}^D(I - \hat{A}\hat{A}^D)(I + \lambda^{-1}\hat{A}\hat{B}^D)^{-1}. \quad (6)$$

The second equality in (5) - (6) is easily verified by a direct calculation.

Since $(I + \lambda\hat{A}^D\hat{B})^{-1}$ can be expanded in a geometric series (Neumann series) in a neighborhood of $\lambda = 0$, we have $\hat{A}^D(I + \lambda\hat{A}^D\hat{B})^{-1} = \hat{A}^D \sum_{k=0}^{\infty} (-1)^k(\hat{A}^D\hat{B})^k\lambda^k$ which is the first term on the right of (4). To get the second term on the right hand side of (4) observe that for any m,

$$I = \sum_{k=0}^{m-1} (-1)^k(\hat{A}\hat{B}^D)^k\lambda^{-k}(I + \lambda^{-1}\hat{A}\hat{B}^D) + (-1)^m\lambda^{-m}(\hat{A}\hat{B}^D)^m.$$

Hence, taking $m = \nu = \mathrm{Ind}(\hat{A})$, we have

$$(I - \lambda^{-1}\hat{A}\hat{B}^D)^{-1} = \sum_{k=0}^{\nu-1} (-1)^k(\hat{A}\hat{B}^D)^k\lambda^{-k} + (-1)^\nu\lambda^{-\nu}(\hat{A}\hat{B}^D)^\nu(I + \lambda^{-1}\hat{A}\hat{B}^D)^{-1}.$$

Multiplying by $\lambda^{-1}\hat{B}^D(I - \hat{A}\hat{A}^D)$ we find that

$$\lambda^{-1}\hat{B}^D(I - \hat{A}\hat{A}^D)(I + \lambda^{-1}\hat{A}\hat{B}^D)^{-1} = \hat{B}^D(I - \hat{A}\hat{A}^D) \sum_{k=0}^{\nu-1} (-1)^k(\hat{A}\hat{B}^D)^k\lambda^{-k-1}$$

since $(I - \hat{A}\hat{A}^D)\hat{A}^\nu = 0$. This is the second term of (4) and (2) follows. Note that if $\nu \neq 0$, then the coefficient of $\lambda^{-\nu}$ is nonzero. □

3. APPLICATION TO DIFFERENTIAL EQUATIONS

In this section we shall consider the initial value problem

$$A\dot{\underline{x}} + B\underline{x} = \underline{f} \quad , \quad 0 \leq t < \infty; \ \underline{x}(0) = \underline{x}_o \tag{1}$$

where $A,B \in \mathbb{C}^{n\times n}$ and $\underline{x}(t)$, $\underline{f}(t) \in \mathbb{C}^{n\times 1}$ for all t. We will be interested not only in the case when $\underline{f}$ is sufficiently smooth and $\underline{x}_o$ is a consistent initial condition but also in the case when $\underline{f}$ may be only piecewise smooth and $\underline{x}_o$ is an arbitrary initial condition.

We shall assume that there exists an s_o such that $s_oA + B$ is invertible. Taking Laplace transforms of both sides of (1) we have $L[\underline{x}] = (sA + B)^{-1}(A\underline{x}_o + L[\underline{f}])$. Using the Laurent expansion (2.2) and (2.5) gives

$$\begin{aligned} L[\underline{x}] &= \hat{A}^D(sI + \hat{A}^D\hat{B})^{-1}(\hat{A}\underline{x}_o + L[\hat{\underline{f}}]) \\ &+ (I - \hat{A}\hat{A}^D)\hat{B}^D\left[\sum_{k=0}^{\nu-1} (-1)^k(\hat{A}\hat{B}^D)^k s^k(\hat{A}\underline{x}_o + L[\hat{\underline{f}}])\right]. \end{aligned} \tag{2}$$

where $\hat{\underline{f}} = (s_oA + B)^{-1}\underline{f}$.

We shall first show how the results of Section 3.2 can be derived from (2). Suppose that $\hat{\underline{f}}$ possesses ν continuous derivatives which have Laplace transforms. Then $s^kL[\hat{\underline{f}}] = L[\hat{\underline{f}}^{(k)}] + \sum_{i=0}^{k-1} s^{k-i-1}\hat{\underline{f}}^{(i)}(0)$, $k = 1,2,\ldots,\nu - 1$, so that (2) becomes

$$\begin{aligned} L[\underline{x}] &= \hat{A}^D(sI + \hat{A}^D\hat{B})^{-1}(\hat{A}\underline{x}_o + L[\underline{f}]) \\ &+ (I - \hat{A}\hat{A}^D)\hat{B}^D \sum_{k=0}^{\nu-1} (-1)^k(\hat{A}\hat{B}^D)^k L[\hat{\underline{f}}^{(k)}] + \underline{p}(s) \end{aligned} \tag{3}$$

where

$$\underline{p}(s) = (I - \hat{A}\hat{A}^D)\hat{B}^D \left\{ \sum_{k=1}^{\nu-1} (-\hat{A}\hat{B}^D)^k [s^k \hat{A}\underline{x}_o + \sum_{i=0}^{k-1} s^{k-i-1} \underline{f}^{(i)}(0)] + \hat{A}\underline{x}_o \right\}. \quad (4)$$

Now for $L[\underline{x}]$ to be the Laplace transform of a continuous function requires that $L[\underline{x}] \to \underline{0}$ as $\mathrm{Re}(s) \to \infty$. But $L[\underline{x}] \to \underline{0}$ as $\mathrm{Re}(s) \to \infty$ if and only if $\underline{p}(s) = \underline{0}$ and this will happen if and only if $\underline{x}_o$ satisfies

$$\hat{B}^D(I - \hat{A}\hat{A}^D)\left[\hat{A}\underline{x}_o - \hat{A}\hat{B}^D \sum_{k=0}^{\nu-2} (-1)^k (\hat{A}\hat{B}^D)^k \hat{\underline{f}}^{(k)}(0)\right] = \underline{0} \quad (5)$$

If $\underline{x}_o$ satisfies (5), then $\underline{p}(s) = \underline{0}$ in (3) and we may take inverse transforms to find that

$$\begin{aligned} \underline{x}(t) = {} & \hat{A}\hat{A}^D e^{-\hat{A}^D\hat{B}t}\underline{x}_o + \hat{A}^D \int_o^t e^{\hat{A}^D\hat{B}(s-t)}\hat{\underline{f}}(s)ds \\ & + (I - \hat{A}\hat{A}^D)\hat{B}^D \sum_{k=0}^{\nu-1} (-1)^k (\hat{A}\hat{B}^D)^k \hat{\underline{f}}^{(k)}(t) \end{aligned} \quad (6)$$

which is (3.1.15) of Theorem 3.1.3 (allowing for the fact that (6) is derived under the assumption that $\underline{x}$ has a Laplace transform). If $\underline{x}$ is to be continuous at zero, $\underline{x}(t) \to \underline{x}_o$ as $t \to 0$ so that we must have

$$\underline{x}_o = \hat{A}\hat{A}^D\underline{x}_o + (I - \hat{A}\hat{A}^D)\hat{B}^D \sum_{k=0}^{\nu-1} (-1)^k (\hat{A}\hat{B}^D)^k \hat{\underline{f}}^{(k)}(0). \quad (7)$$

It can be shown that if (7) is satisfied, then (5) is satisfied. Thus (7) characterizes consistent initial conditions and if $\underline{x}_o$ satisfies (7), the unique solution is given by (6).

On the other hand, as described in Section 2, one is sometimes interested in the impulsive behavior of systems.

So suppose that one has (1) with $\underline{f}$ possessing ν continuous derivatives which have Laplace transforms but with an $\underline{x}(0)$ that does not satisfy (7).

This could happen if a circuit is assembled at time t = 0 from other circuits or subsystems. Thus while $A\dot{\underline{x}} + B\underline{x} = \underline{f}$ may govern the dynamics for $t > 0$, $\underline{x}(0^-)$ is determined by the state of the previous systems.

In this case, we have that $\underline{x} = \underline{x}_c + \underline{x}_i$ where $\underline{x}_c$ is given by the right hand side of (6) and the impulsive part, $\underline{x}_i$ is determined by taking the inverse Laplace transform of (4) so that

$$\underline{x}_i(t) = (I-\hat{A}^D\hat{A})\hat{B}^D \sum_{k=0}^{\nu-1} (-\hat{A}\hat{B}^D)^k \left(\delta^{(k)}(t)\hat{A}\underline{x}_o + \sum_{i=0}^{k-1} \delta^{(k-i-1)}(t)\underline{\hat{f}}^{(i)}(0)\right).$$

When A is nonsingular, the solution of (1) is continuous if $\underline{f}$ is even piecewise continuous. However, when A is singular, the situation is different. The $\underline{\hat{f}}^{(k)}(t)$ terms in (6) will involve either delta functions if $\underline{\hat{f}}^{(k-2)}$ is only piecewise continuous or perhaps more general types of distributions then delta functions if $\underline{\hat{f}}^{(k-2)}$ is not piecewise continuous.

If $\underline{\hat{f}}^{(k-2)}$ is not piecewise continuous, but $L[\underline{\hat{f}}]s^{-\ell} \to \underline{0}$ as $\mathrm{Re}(s) \to \infty$ for some integer ℓ ($L[\underline{f}]$ has at most a pole at infinity), then the inverse Laplace transform can be taken in (3) to again give $\underline{x} = \underline{x}_c + \underline{x}_i$, where $\underline{x}_i$ involves $\delta^{(j)}$ for j up to possibly $k + \ell$.

For an extensive treatment of this impulsive behavior corresponding to poles at infinity see Verghese's thesis [63]. It was Verghese that first observed that our results on characterizing the consistent initial conditions for $A\dot{\underline{x}} + B\underline{x} = \underline{f}$ were actually a characterization of which initial condition led to impulsive behavior and which did not.

We shall conclude this chapter by returning to the elementary, but instructive example, of Section 2.3. Again consider a simple circuit consisting of a constant nonzero voltage source E and a capacitor of capacitance C. At time t = 0 the capacitor is shorted out. Let

$$h(t) = \begin{cases} E \text{ if } t < 0 \\ 0 \text{ if } t \geq 0 \end{cases} .$$

Then the equation for the charge on the capacitor is

$$0\dot{q} + \frac{1}{C} q = h(t). \tag{8}$$

In this case q has a jump discontinuity at zero and the current $i = \dot{q} = -CE\delta(t)$ has an impulse at $t = 0$. Suppose on the other hand that the circuit also has a resistor R in series with the capacitor and at time $t = 0$ the short is across the voltage source so that the appropriate equation is

$$R\dot{q} + \frac{1}{C} q = h(t). \tag{9}$$

In this case q is continuous for all time and i has only a jump discontinuity at $t = 0$ and no impulsive behavior.

Since $R \neq 0$ in (9), (9) is, in our nomenclature, a nonsingular system. On the other hand, since the coefficient of $\dot{q}$ in (8) is zero, (8) is a singular system and is able to exhibit impulsive behavior. If R is small, then the relationship between (8) and (9) can be considered a singular perturbation problem.

5 Singular perturbations

1. INTRODUCTION

As discussed in Section 6 of Chapter 2, singular perturbation problems arise in a variety of applications. Consider

$$\begin{aligned} \dot{\underline{x}} &= A_1(\varepsilon)\underline{x} + A_2(\varepsilon)\underline{y} + \underline{u}_1 \\ \varepsilon\dot{\underline{y}} &= B_1(\varepsilon)\underline{x} + B_2(\varepsilon)\underline{y} + \underline{u}_2 \end{aligned} \tag{1}$$

where $A_i(\varepsilon)$, $B_i(\varepsilon)$ are matrices, $\underline{x}$ and $\underline{y}$ are column vectors and $\varepsilon > 0$. System (1) may be considered as part of an initial or boundary value problem, or the process in a control problem.

Basic to understanding (1) is the associated homogeneous system,

$$\begin{aligned} \dot{\underline{x}} &= A_1(\varepsilon)\underline{x} + A_2(\varepsilon)\underline{y} \\ \varepsilon\dot{\underline{y}} &= B_1(\varepsilon)\underline{x} + B_2(\varepsilon)\underline{y} \end{aligned} \; . \tag{2}$$

When $\varepsilon = 0$ in (2), we obtain the reduced system

$$\begin{aligned} \dot{\underline{x}} &= A_1(0)\underline{x} + A_2(0)\underline{y} \\ \underline{0} &= B_1(0)\underline{x} + B_2(0)\underline{y} \end{aligned} \; . \tag{3}$$

Note that (3) is a singular system of equations. Sufficient conditions are known [58] for solutions of (1) to converge as $\varepsilon \to 0^+$ to a solution of (3) for $t > 0$. We shall present both necessary and sufficient conditions for such convergence and in addition obtain an explicit formula for the limit.

Equation (2) may be rewritten as

$$\frac{d}{dt}\begin{bmatrix} \underline{x} \\ \underline{y} \end{bmatrix} = (A(\varepsilon) + B(\varepsilon)/\varepsilon)\begin{bmatrix} \underline{x} \\ \underline{y} \end{bmatrix}, \quad \varepsilon > 0 \tag{4}$$

where $A(\varepsilon) = \begin{bmatrix} A_1(\varepsilon) & A_2(\varepsilon) \\ 0 & 0 \end{bmatrix}$, $B(\varepsilon) = \begin{bmatrix} 0 & 0 \\ B_1(\varepsilon) & B_2(\varepsilon) \end{bmatrix}$. The fundamental solution of (4) will be important in studying (1). The fundamental solution is

$$X_\varepsilon(t) = e^{(A(\varepsilon) + B(\varepsilon)/\varepsilon)t}. \tag{5}$$

Thus our first problem may be reformulated as follows: to determine necessary and sufficient conditions for (5) to converge as $\varepsilon > 0^+$ for $t > 0$ and to find an explicit formula for the limit. We shall then develop an asymptotic expansion for (5) under these conditions. Then we shall discuss the case when several different negative powers of ε are present. Finally we shall consider more general singularly perturbed systems of the form,

$$A(\varepsilon)\dot{\underline{x}} + B(\varepsilon)\underline{x} = \underline{f}. \tag{6}$$

In expressing our results, it will be convenient to have the following notation. For $A,B \in \mathbb{C}^{m\times m}$, let $[A;B] = (I - B^D B)A(I - B^D B)$. Note that $[I,B] = I - BB^D$ and $(I - BB^D)B = [B;B]$.

2. <u>$e^{(A + B/\varepsilon)t}$; EXISTENCE OF LIMIT</u>

Recall that a matrix A is called <u>stable</u> if all eigenvalues have negative real part. A is stable if and only if $e^{At} \to 0$ as $t \to \infty$. We need a generalization of this concept. A matrix A is called <u>semistable</u> if A has index 0 or 1 and all non-zero eigenvalues have negative real part. That A is semistable if and only if e^{At} converges as $t \to \infty$ follows easily from the Jordan canonical form for A.

Re, Im refer to real and imaginary parts of complex numbers. If Σ is a set of complex numbers, then $\mathrm{Re}\Sigma = \{\mathrm{Re}\lambda : \lambda \in \Sigma\}$. For sets of complex numbers Σ, Σ' we let $\rho(\Sigma, \Sigma') = \inf\{|\alpha - \alpha'| : \alpha \in \Sigma \quad \alpha' \in \Sigma'\}$.

The following inequality concerning the numerical range, $W(A)$, will be needed:

$$0 < \rho(\lambda, W(A)) \leq \|(\lambda - A)^{-1}\| \quad \text{for } \lambda \notin W(A). \tag{1}$$

To prove (1), note that $W(A)$ is a compact set. Thus $0 < \rho(\lambda, W(A))$ $= \inf\{|\lambda - \mu| : \mu \in W(A)\} = \inf\{|(\lambda \underline{x} - A\underline{x}, \underline{x})| : \|\underline{x}\| = 1\}$ since the continuous function $f(\mu) = |\lambda - \mu|$ achieves its minimum on $W(A)$. Using the Schwartz inequality we get $\rho(\lambda, W(A)) \leq \inf\{\|(\lambda - A)\underline{x}\| : \|\underline{x}\| = 1\}$. Inequality (1) now follows from Theorem 6.5.1 of [46].

For notational convenience, it is easiest to study (1.5) with A,B independent of ε. The more general case will follow quickly. The major result of this section is

<u>Theorem 5.2.1</u> Suppose that A,B are $n \times n$ matrices. Let $X_\varepsilon(t) = e^{(A + B/\varepsilon)t}$. Then $X_\varepsilon(t)$ converges pointwise as $\varepsilon \to 0^+$ for all $t \geq 0$, if and only if B is semistable. If B is semistable, then

$$\lim_{\varepsilon \to 0^+} e^{(A + B/\varepsilon)t} = e^{(I - BB^D)At}(I - BB^D). \tag{2}$$

Before proving Theorem 1, consider the following example.

<u>Example 5.2.1</u> Let $A = \begin{bmatrix} 0 & 0 \\ 0 & 2\pi i \end{bmatrix}$, $B = \begin{bmatrix} 0 & 1 \\ 0 & 0 \end{bmatrix}$. Then $\mathrm{Ind}(B) = 2$ so that B is not semistable. By Theorem 1, the limit (2) will fail to exist for all $t \geq 0$. However,

$$e^{(A + B/\varepsilon)t} = \begin{bmatrix} 1 & [e^{2\pi it} - 1]/2\pi i\varepsilon \\ 0 & e^{2\pi it} \end{bmatrix}$$

so that a limit exists for t an integer. In studying (2), however, it is of interest to know when (2) exists for all $t \geq 0$ and the semistability of B is necessary.

We shall first prove the sufficiency of semistability.

<u>Theorem 5.2.2</u> If B is semistable, then

$$\lim_{\varepsilon\to 0^+} e^{A+B/\varepsilon} = e^{(I - BB^D)A}(I - BB^D) = (I - BB^D)e^{A(I - BB^D)}. \tag{3}$$

<u>Proof</u> Suppose B is semistable. If $B = 0$, then (3) is immediate. If B is invertible, then (3) is known; however, it may also be proved by the same techniques we use. Assume then that $0 \in \sigma(B)$ and $B \neq 0$.

Note that if T is any nonsingular matrix (independent of ε), then $\exp(A + B/\varepsilon) = T^{-1}\exp(TAT^{-1} + (TBT^{-1})/\varepsilon)T$. It follows that a simultaneous similarity may be applied to A and B without affecting our results.

Assume then that B is already in Jordan form, $B = \mathrm{diag}(\tilde{B}_{11},0)$, where $\tilde{B}_{11}$ is nonsingular and has its "ones" on the subdiagonal and $\mathrm{Re}\sigma(\tilde{B}_{11}) < 0$. As observed in Section 2 of Chapter 1, another similarity gives $\mathrm{diag}(B_{11},0)$ where $\mathrm{ReW}(B_{11}) < -\beta$ for some $\beta > 0$. Assume then $B = \begin{bmatrix} B_{11} & 0 \\ 0 & 0 \end{bmatrix}$ and $A = \begin{bmatrix} A_{11} & A_{12} \\ A_{21} & A_{22} \end{bmatrix}$. β is now fixed.

To calculate the limit (3) we shall use the Cauchy integral formula

$$e^{A+B/\varepsilon} = \frac{1}{2\pi i}\int_{C(\varepsilon)} e^{\lambda}(\lambda - A - B/\varepsilon)^{-1}d\lambda \tag{4}$$

where $C(\varepsilon)$ is a contour containing $\sigma(A + B/\varepsilon)$ in its interior. Therefore, it is necessary to obtain information about $\sigma(A + B/\varepsilon)$. The needed information is contained in the following two Lemmas. The first is just the Gerschgorin theorem for block matrices [27].

Lemma 5.2.1 For $\varepsilon > 0$ and A,B given by (4), $\sigma(A + B/\varepsilon) \subseteq G_0 \cup G_1(\varepsilon)$ where

$$G_0 = \{z : \|(z - A_{22})^{-1}\|^{-1} \leq \|A_{22}\|\},$$

$$G_1(\varepsilon) = \{z : \|(z - A_{11} - B_{11}/\varepsilon)^{-1}\|^{-1} \leq \|A_{12}\|\}.$$

Let $\varepsilon_0 > 0$ be such that $\frac{\beta}{\varepsilon_0} > \|A_{11}\| + \|A_{12}\| + \|A_{21}\| + \|A_{22}\| + 3$.

Lemma 5.2.2 For $0 < \varepsilon \leq \varepsilon_0$, there exist two circles C_0 and $C_1(\varepsilon)$ such that G_0 is contained in the interior of C_0 and $G_1(\varepsilon)$ is contained in the interior of $C_1(\varepsilon)$. Furthermore, $\rho(C_0, C_1(\varepsilon)) \geq 1$ and $\mathrm{Re}C_1(\varepsilon) < -\beta/\varepsilon$.

Proof of Lemma 2 Since $\mathrm{Re}W(B_{11}) < -\beta$ for some $\beta > 0$, it follows that $\mathrm{Re}W(B_{11}/\varepsilon) < -\beta/\varepsilon$. Thus there exists $\gamma > 0$ so that the circle $\tilde{C}_1(\varepsilon)$ with center at $(-(\gamma + \beta)/\varepsilon, 0)$ and radius γ/ε contains $W(B_{11}/\varepsilon)$ in its interior. Now using (1) and the triangle inequality it follows that for $\mu \in G_1(\varepsilon)$, $\rho(\mu, W(B_{11}/\varepsilon)) \leq \|A_{11}\| + \|A_{12}\|$. Therefore the circle $C_1(\varepsilon)$ with center at $(-(\gamma + \beta)/\varepsilon, 0)$ and radius $r_1(\varepsilon) = \gamma/\varepsilon + \|A_{11}\| + \|A_{12}\| + 1$ contains $G_1(\varepsilon)$ in its interior and for $0 < \varepsilon \leq \varepsilon_0$, $\mathrm{Re}C_1(\varepsilon) < -\beta/\varepsilon$.

Similarly one can show that for $\mu \in G_0$, $|\mu| < \|A_{21}\| + \|A_{22}\|$. Therefore, the circle C_0 with center at $(0,0)$ and radius $r_0 = \|A_{12}\| + \|A_{22}\| + 1$ contains G_0 in its interior. Also we have $\rho(C_0, C_1(\varepsilon)) = (\gamma + \beta)/\varepsilon - r_1(\varepsilon) - r_0 \geq 1$. □

For the rest of the proof of Theorem 2, assume that $0 < \varepsilon \leq \varepsilon_0$. We now proceed to establish (3). From (4) and Lemmas 1, 2 we have $e^{A+B/\varepsilon} = I_0(\varepsilon) + I_1(\varepsilon)$ where

$$I_0(\varepsilon) = \frac{1}{2\pi i} \int_{C_0} e^{\lambda}(\lambda - A - B/\varepsilon)^{-1} d\lambda, \tag{5}$$

$$I_1(\varepsilon) = \frac{1}{2\pi i} \int_{C_1(\varepsilon)} e^{\lambda}(\lambda - A - B/\varepsilon)^{-1} d\lambda. \tag{6}$$

Consider (6). Let $\zeta = \varepsilon\lambda$ to obtain $I_1(\varepsilon) = \frac{1}{2\pi i} \int_{\hat{C}_1(\varepsilon)} e^{\frac{\zeta}{\varepsilon}}(\zeta - \varepsilon A - B)^{-1} d\zeta$ where $\hat{C}_1(\varepsilon)$ is the circle with center at $(-(\gamma + \beta), 0)$ and radius $\gamma + \varepsilon k$, $k = \|A_{11}\| + \|A_{12}\| + 1$. Thus

$$\|I_1(\varepsilon)\| \leq \frac{1}{2\pi} 2\pi(\gamma + \varepsilon k)e^{-\beta/\varepsilon} \sup\{\|(\zeta - \varepsilon A - B)^{-1}\| : \zeta \in \hat{C}_1(\varepsilon)\}. \tag{7}$$

Since $\|(\zeta - \varepsilon A - B)^{-1}\| \to \|(\zeta - B)\|^{-1}$ as $\varepsilon \to 0^+$, $\|(\zeta - \varepsilon A - B)^{-1}\|$ is bounded independent of ε for $\zeta \in \hat{C}_1(\varepsilon)$. Thus $\|I_1(\varepsilon)\| \leq Me^{-\beta/\varepsilon}$ for some $M > 0$ and $I_1(\varepsilon) \to 0$ as $\varepsilon \to 0^+$.

Next consider (5), which may be written $I_0(\varepsilon) = e^{A+B/\varepsilon}P_0(\varepsilon)$, where

$$P_0(\varepsilon) = \frac{1}{2\pi i} \int_{C_0} (\lambda - A - B/\varepsilon)^{-1} d\lambda. \tag{8}$$

Since $P_0(\varepsilon)$ is a projection which commutes with $A + B/\varepsilon$, we have $I_0(\varepsilon) = e^{F_0(\varepsilon)} P_0(\varepsilon)$ where

$$F_0(\varepsilon) = (A + B/\varepsilon)P_0(\varepsilon) = \frac{1}{2\pi i} \int_{C_0} \lambda(\lambda - A - B/\varepsilon)^{-1} d\lambda. \tag{9}$$

In (8), let $\zeta = \varepsilon\lambda$ to obtain

$$P_0(\varepsilon) = \frac{1}{2\pi i} \int_{\hat{C}_0(\varepsilon)} (\zeta - \varepsilon A - B)^{-1} d\zeta = \frac{1}{2\pi i} \int_{\hat{C}_0(\varepsilon_0)} (\zeta - \varepsilon A - B)^{-1} d\zeta \quad (10)$$

where $\hat{C}_0(\varepsilon)$ is a circle with center at the origin and radius εr_0. Since $\hat{C}(\varepsilon_0)$ does not contain any of $W(B_{11})$ we have

$\operatorname{Lim}_{\varepsilon \to 0^+} P_0(\varepsilon) = \frac{1}{2\pi i} \int_{\hat{C}_0(\varepsilon_0)} (\zeta - B)^{-1} d\zeta$. Since B has index 1, Theorem 4.21

gives

$$(\zeta - B)^{-1} = -(I - \zeta B^D)^{-1} B^D + \zeta^{-1}(I - BB^D). \quad (11)$$

Thus the integral may be evaluated using the residue theorem to obtain $\operatorname{Lim}_{\varepsilon \to 0^+} P_0(\varepsilon) = I - BB^D$. In (9), let $\zeta = \varepsilon\lambda$ to obtain,

$$\begin{aligned} F_0(\varepsilon) &= \frac{1}{2\pi i} \int_{\hat{C}_0(\varepsilon_0)} \frac{\zeta}{\varepsilon} (\zeta - \varepsilon A - B)^{-1} d\zeta \\ &= \frac{1}{2\pi i} \int_{\hat{C}_0(\varepsilon_0)} \frac{\zeta}{\varepsilon} \{(\zeta - \varepsilon A - B)^{-1} \varepsilon A (\zeta - B)^{-1} + (\zeta - B)^{-1}\} d\zeta \end{aligned} \quad (12)$$

Thus $F_0(\varepsilon) = \frac{1}{2\pi i} \int_{\hat{C}_0} (\zeta - B)^{-1} A (\zeta - B)^{-1} d\zeta + \frac{1}{2\pi i} \int_{\hat{C}_0} \frac{\zeta}{\varepsilon} (\zeta - B)^{-1} d\zeta + O(\varepsilon)$.

From (11) we see that the integrand of the second integral is analytic inside $\hat{C}_0$ and the integral is zero. The first integral can be evaluated by residues using (11). Thus $\operatorname{Lim}_{\varepsilon \to 0^+} F_0(\varepsilon) = (I - BB^D)A(I - BB^D) = [A;B]$. Therefore,

$$\operatorname{Lim}_{\varepsilon \to 0^+} I(\varepsilon) = \operatorname{Lim}_{\varepsilon \to 0^+} I_0(\varepsilon) = e^{[A;B]}[I;B] = e^{[I;B]A}[I;B]. \quad \square$$

<u>Completion of proof of Theorem 1</u> We need to show the necessity of semi-stability. Assume that $X_\varepsilon(t)$ has a pointwise limit as $\varepsilon \to 0^+$ for $t \geq 0$. As observed in the proof of Theorem 2, we may assume that a similarity

transformation has been performed on B so that $B = \mathrm{diag}(J_1,\ldots,J_r,N)$ where $\sigma(J_i) = \lambda_i$, $\sigma(N) = 0$, $\lambda_i \neq \lambda_j$ if $i \neq j$, $\lambda_i \neq 0$, $i = 1,\ldots,r$. In addition, we may assume that $W(J_i)$ is in the open left-half plane if $\mathrm{Re}\lambda_i < 0$, $W(J_i)$ is in the open right-half plane if $\mathrm{Re}\lambda_i > 0$ and $W(J_i) \cap W(J_j) = \phi$ if $i \neq j$, $i = 1,2,\ldots,r$. Let $\lambda_0 = 0$ if the nilpotent block N is present. From [27] and the same reasoning used in the proof of Theorem 2, for $i = 1,2,\ldots,r$, there exists $\lambda_\varepsilon(i) \in \sigma(A + B/\varepsilon)$ such that $|\lambda_\varepsilon(i) - \lambda_i/\varepsilon| \leq K_i + \delta_i/\varepsilon$, where K_i and δ_i are constants.

First we show that $\mathrm{Re}\lambda \leq 0$ for $\lambda \in \sigma(B)$. Suppose that $\lambda \in \sigma(B)$ and $\mathrm{Re}\lambda > 0$. Then there exists $\lambda_\varepsilon \in \sigma(A + B/\varepsilon)$ such that $\mathrm{Re}\lambda_\varepsilon \to +\infty$. Let $\underline{\phi}_\varepsilon$ be such that $(A + B/\varepsilon)\underline{\phi}_\varepsilon = \lambda_\varepsilon \underline{\phi}_\varepsilon$, $\|\underline{\phi}_\varepsilon\| = 1$. Then $\|e^{(A + B/\varepsilon)}\underline{\phi}_\varepsilon\|$ $= \|e^{\lambda_\varepsilon}\underline{\phi}_\varepsilon\| \to \infty$ which is a contradiction.

Some further calculations are necessary before we can rule out the possibility that $\mathrm{Re}\lambda_i = 0$, $i \neq 0$. Using [27], we can argue as in the proof of Theorem 2 that for ε less than some ε_0 there exists contours $C_i(\varepsilon)$, $C_0(\varepsilon)$ which do not intersect such that $W(J_i/\varepsilon_0) \subseteq \text{Interior }(C_i(\varepsilon))$, $W(N/\varepsilon) \subseteq \text{Interior }(C_0(\varepsilon))$, $\sigma(A + B/\varepsilon) \subset \bigcup_i \text{Interior }(C_i(\varepsilon))$, and $\rho(W(J_i/\varepsilon),C_i(\varepsilon))$, $\rho(W(N/\varepsilon),C_0(\varepsilon))$ are bounded independent of ε. Thus each $C_i(\varepsilon)$ contains only those eigenvalues of $A + B/\varepsilon$ that are clustering 'near' those of J_i/ε. Then $X_\varepsilon(t) = \sum_{i=0}^{r} e^{F_i(\varepsilon)t} P_i(\varepsilon)$ where

$$P_i(\varepsilon) = \frac{1}{2\pi i}\int_{C_i(\varepsilon)} (\lambda - A - B/\varepsilon)^{-1} d\lambda,$$ and $$F_i(\varepsilon) = (A + B/\varepsilon)P_0(\varepsilon) = \frac{1}{2\pi i}\int_{C_i(\varepsilon)} \lambda(\lambda - A - B/\varepsilon)^{-1} d\lambda.$$ As in the proof of Theorem 2, it follows that $P_i(\varepsilon) \to I - (\lambda_i - B)^D(\lambda_i - B)$. Since $X_\varepsilon(t)$ has a limit for $t > 0$, so does $X_\varepsilon(t)P_i(\varepsilon)$. Thus $e^{F_i(\varepsilon)t}$ has a pointwise limit for $t > 0$ for each i.

We shall show that

$$F_i(\varepsilon) = \lambda_i P_i(\varepsilon)/\varepsilon + G(\varepsilon) + (\lambda_i - B)[I - (\lambda_i - B)^D(\lambda_i - B)]/\varepsilon, \tag{13}$$

where $G(\varepsilon)$ is continuous at zero.

Assume for the moment that (13) holds. We shall use this to show that we cannot have $\mathrm{Re}\lambda_i = 0$, $i \neq 0$, and that B has index 0 or 1.

Note that $P_i(\varepsilon)$ is idempotent and the last term in (13) is nilpotent, so that $\mathrm{Trace}(F_i(\varepsilon)) = \mu_i\lambda_i/\varepsilon + \mathrm{Trace}(G_i(\varepsilon))$ where μ_i is an integer. Assume that $\mathrm{Re}\lambda_i = 0$ and $\mathrm{Im}\lambda_i \neq 0$. Then there exists a $\mu(\varepsilon) \in \sigma(F_i(\varepsilon))$ such that $\mathrm{Re}(\mu(\varepsilon))$ is bounded and $|\mathrm{Im}\mu(\varepsilon)| \to \infty$. Let $\underline{\phi}(\varepsilon)$ be an eigenvector of $F_i(\varepsilon)$ corresponding to $\mu(\varepsilon)$ and assume $\|\underline{\phi}(\varepsilon)\| = 1$. Pick a subsequence $\underline{\phi}(\varepsilon_k)$ so that $\underline{\phi}(\varepsilon_k)$ converges. Then $(e^{F_i(\varepsilon_k)t}\underline{\phi}(\varepsilon_k),\underline{\phi}(\varepsilon_k)) = e^{\mu(\varepsilon_k)t}$ converges for all $t > 0$ which is a contradiction. Thus $\mathrm{Re}\lambda_i < 0$, $i = 1,\ldots,r$.

Now consider (13) for $i = 0$. Since $\lambda_0 = 0$ we have $F_0(\varepsilon) = G_0(\varepsilon) + Q/\varepsilon$, where $Q = B(I - BB^D)$. Since $\mathrm{Trace}(F_0(\varepsilon)) = \mathrm{Trace}(G_0(\varepsilon))$, we must have that $\sigma(F_0(\varepsilon))$ is bounded. Pick t_1 such that $|\mathrm{Im}\sigma((G_0(\varepsilon) + Q/\varepsilon)t_1)| \leq \frac{\pi}{2}$. Let Ln be the principal branch of $\ell n\, z$. Then if $e^{(G_0(\varepsilon) + Q/\varepsilon)t_1} \to Q$ we have $(G_0(\varepsilon) + Q/\varepsilon)t_1 = \mathrm{Ln}\, e^{(G_0(\varepsilon) + Q/\varepsilon)t_1} \to \mathrm{Ln}Q$. However, if $Q \neq 0$, the left-hand side cannot possess a limit. Thus $Q = B(I - BB^D) = 0$ and B has index zero or one.

Hence it suffices to show that (13) holds for Theorem 1 to be proven. Let $\tilde{B} = B - \lambda_i$, and $\zeta = \varepsilon\lambda - \lambda_i$. Then,

$$(F_i(\varepsilon) - \lambda_i/\varepsilon)P_i(\varepsilon) = \frac{1}{2\pi i}\int_{C_i(\varepsilon)} (\lambda - \lambda_i/\varepsilon)(\lambda - A - B/\varepsilon)^{-1}d\lambda$$

$$= \frac{1}{2\pi i}\int_{\hat{C}_i(\varepsilon)} \frac{\zeta}{\varepsilon}(\zeta - \varepsilon A - B)^{-1}d\zeta,$$

where $C_i(\varepsilon)$ is a circle with center at the origin which does not contain any nonzero eigenvalues of $\tilde{B}$. Hence as in the proof of Theorem 2:

$$F_i(\varepsilon) = \frac{\lambda_i}{\varepsilon} P_i(\varepsilon) + \frac{1}{2\pi i} \int_{\hat{C}_i} \zeta(\zeta - A - \tilde{B})^{-1} A(\zeta - \tilde{B}) d\zeta$$

$$+ \frac{1}{2\pi i} \int_{\hat{C}_i} \frac{\zeta}{\varepsilon} (\zeta - \tilde{B})^{-1} d\lambda.$$

The first integral is a continuous function of ε and the second can be evaluated to yield $\tilde{B}(I - \tilde{B}^D\tilde{B})/\varepsilon$. Thus (13) follows. □

3. $e^{(A + B/\varepsilon)t}$; THE ASYMPTOTIC EXPANSION

Assume that B is semistable. From Section 2 we have

$$\exp((A + B/\varepsilon)t) = \exp(F_1(\varepsilon)t)P_1(\varepsilon) + \exp(F_2(\varepsilon)t)P_2(\varepsilon) \qquad (1)$$

where $\exp(F_j(\varepsilon)t) = \frac{1}{2\pi i} \int_{C_j} \exp(\lambda t)(\lambda - A - B/\varepsilon)^{-1} d\lambda$,

$P_j(\varepsilon) = \frac{1}{2\pi i} \int_{C_j} (\lambda - A - B/\varepsilon)^{-1} d\lambda$. C_1 a "small" contour around zero and C_2 a contour around $\{\sigma(B) \cup \sigma(A + B/\varepsilon)\} \setminus \{0\}$. Since

$F_1(\varepsilon) = \frac{1}{2\pi i} \int_{C_1} \gamma(\gamma - \varepsilon A - B)^{-1} A(\gamma - B)^{-1} d\gamma$, $F_1(\varepsilon)$ is an analytic function of ε and we may write

$$\exp(F_1(\varepsilon)t)P_1(\varepsilon) = \sum_{k=0}^{\infty} X_k(t)\varepsilon^k \quad , \quad t \geq 0. \qquad (2)$$

From Theorem 5.2.1,

$$X_o(t) = \exp((I - BB^D)At)(I - BB^D). \qquad (3)$$

Letting $\tau = t/\varepsilon$, we get

$$\exp(F_2(\varepsilon)t)P_2(\varepsilon) = \exp(\varepsilon F_2(\varepsilon)\tau)P_2(\varepsilon) = \frac{1}{2\pi i}\int_{\tilde{C}_2} \exp(\gamma\tau)(\gamma - \varepsilon A - B)^{-1}d\gamma,$$

$\tilde{C}_2$ an appropriate contour around the nonzero eigenvalues of B but not including zero. But $\varepsilon F_2(\varepsilon) = \frac{1}{2\pi i}\int_{\tilde{C}_2} \gamma(\gamma - \varepsilon A - B)^{-1}d\gamma$ is analytic in ε also since $\gamma - B$ is invertible on $\tilde{C}_2$.

Hence

$$\exp(\varepsilon F_2(\varepsilon)\tau)P_2(\varepsilon) = \sum_{k=0}^{\infty} Y_k(\tau)\varepsilon^k. \tag{4}$$

The series (2) and (4) are what are usually referred to as the inner and outer solutions, respectively. To calculate the X_k, Y_k, first note that $F_1(\varepsilon)F_2(\varepsilon) = F_2(\varepsilon)F_1(\varepsilon) = 0$ and both $F_i(\varepsilon)$ commute with $A + B/\varepsilon$. Hence both (2) and (4) are solutions of

$$\frac{dZ}{dt} = (A + B/\varepsilon)Z \quad \text{for } t \geq 0. \tag{5}$$

<u>Calculation of $X_k(t)$</u> Inserting (2) into (5) and equating powers of ε gives that the $X_k(t)$ must satisfy the system of differential equations;

$$BX_o = 0, \tag{6}$$

$$AX_k + BX_{k+1} = \dot{X}_k \quad , \quad k \geq 0. \tag{7:k}$$

Note that $X_o(t)$ given by (3) satisfies (6). To determine $X_1(t)$, notice that from (7:0),

$$B^DBX_1 = B^D\dot{X}_o - B^DAX_1 = -B^DA\exp([A;B]t)[I;B]. \tag{8}$$

While from (7:1), and the assumption that $\mathrm{Ind}(B) = 1$,

$$[I;B]\dot{X}_1 = [I;B]AX_1 = [A;B]X_1 + [I;B]AB^DBX_1. \tag{9}$$

Now B^DBX_1 is given by (8), so that (9) gives

$$[I;B]X_1 = \exp([A;B]t)\int_0^t \exp(-[A;B]s)[I;B]AB^DB(-B^DA)\exp([A;B]s)[I;B]ds$$

$$+ \exp([A;B]t)[I;B]X_1(0).$$

That is,

$$\begin{aligned} X_1(t) = &-\exp([A;B]t)\int_0^t \exp(-[A;B]s)[I;B]AB^DA\exp([A;B]s)[I;B]ds \\ &+ \exp([A;B]t)[I;B]X_1(0) - B^DA\exp([A;B]t)[I;B]. \end{aligned} \tag{10}$$

In the same manner, using (7:k-1) to get B^DBX_k and (7:k) for $[I;B]X_k$ we have

$$\begin{aligned} X_{k+1}(t) = &\exp([A;B]t)\int_0^t \exp(-[A;B]s)[I;B]A[B^D\dot{X}_k - B^DAX_k]ds \\ &+ B^D\dot{X}_k - B^DAX_k + \exp([A;B]t)[I;B]X_{k+1}(0). \end{aligned} \tag{11}$$

To complete the determination of the $X_k(t)$ we need the $X_k(0)$. From (2),

$$\sum_{k=0}^{\infty} X_k(0)\varepsilon^k = \frac{1}{2\pi i}\int_C (\gamma - \varepsilon A - B)^{-1}d\gamma$$

$$= \sum_{k=0}^{\infty} \varepsilon^k \frac{1}{2\pi i}\int_C [(\gamma - B)^{-1}A]^k(\gamma - B)^{-1}d\gamma.$$

Hence

$$X_k(0) = \frac{1}{2\pi i}\int_C [(\gamma - B)^{-1}A]^k(\gamma - B)^{-1}d\gamma \quad , \quad k \geq 0, \tag{12}$$

C a contour around zero containing no nonzero eigenvalues of B inside. In particular, $X_0(0) = \frac{1}{2\pi i}\int_C (\gamma - B)^{-1}d\gamma = [I;B]$ as noted earlier.

Since only $[I;B]X_k(0)$ is needed in (12) some calculation can be saved for $k \geq 1$ by observing that

$$[I;B]X_k(0) = [I;B]A \frac{1}{2\pi i} \int_C [(\gamma - B)^{-1}A]^{k-1}(\gamma - B)^{-1}\gamma^{-1}d\gamma. \tag{13}$$

In particular,

$$[I;B]X_1(0) = [I;B]A \frac{1}{2\pi i} \int_C (\gamma - B)^{-1}\gamma^{-1}d\gamma = -[I;B]AB^D. \tag{14}$$

We shall show one way to evaluate (13) by computing two integrals we shall need later. The same methods may be applied to (13) to give, for example,

$$[I;B]X_2(0) = [I;B]A\{B^DAB^D - (B^D)^2A[I;B] - [I;B]A(B^D)^2\}.$$

<u>Proposition 5.3.1</u> If $\text{Ind}(C) = 1$, then for small enough contours around zero, $\frac{1}{2\pi i} \int \gamma(\gamma - C)^{-1}A(\gamma - C)^{-1}d\gamma = [A;C]$.

<u>Proof</u> By first performing a similarity we may assume $C = \begin{bmatrix} \hat{C} & 0 \\ 0 & 0 \end{bmatrix}$, $\hat{C}$ invertible, and $A = \begin{bmatrix} A_{11} & A_{12} \\ A_{21} & A_{22} \end{bmatrix}$. Then

$$\gamma(\gamma - C)^{-1}A(\gamma - C)^{-1} = \begin{bmatrix} \gamma(\gamma - \hat{C})^{-1}A_{11}(\gamma - \hat{C})^{-1} & (\gamma - \hat{C})^{-1}A_{12} \\ A_{21}(\gamma - \hat{C})^{-1} & A_{22}/\gamma \end{bmatrix}$$ which integrates to $\begin{bmatrix} 0 & 0 \\ 0 & A_{22} \end{bmatrix}$ since $(\gamma - C)^{-1}$ is analytic at zero. □

Similarly, it's easy to show;

<u>Proposition 5.3.2</u> Suppose that $\text{Ind}(C) = 1$. Let C be written as $\begin{bmatrix} \hat{C} & 0 \\ 0 & 0 \end{bmatrix}$. Let $B = [B_{ij}]$, $A = [A_{ij}]$, $i,j = 1,2$. Then for small contours around zero

$$\frac{1}{2\pi i}\int_C \gamma(\gamma-C)^{-1}A(\gamma-C)^{-1}B(\gamma-C)^{-1}d\gamma = -\begin{bmatrix} 0 & \hat{C}^{-1}A_{12}B_{22} \\ A_{22}B_{21}\hat{C}^{-1} & A_{21}\hat{C}^{-1}B_{12} \end{bmatrix}. \quad (15)$$

Calculation of $Y_k(t)$ Since $\tau = t/\varepsilon$, $\sum_{k=0}^{\infty} \varepsilon^k Y_k$ satisfies $\frac{dZ}{dt} = (\varepsilon A + B)Z$. Substituting the series into the differential equation and equating powers of ε gives the infinite system

$$\dot{Y}_o = BY_o, \qquad k = 0 \qquad (16{:}0)$$

$$\dot{Y}_k = BY_k + AY_{k-1}, \qquad k \geq 1.$$

(16:k) can be easily solved iteratively provided the initial values $Y_k(0)$ are known to give

$$Y_k(t) = \exp(Bt)\int_o^t \exp(-Bs)AY_{k-1}(s)ds + \exp(Bt)Y_k(0) \qquad (17)$$

Note, however, that $\exp(\varepsilon F_2(\varepsilon)\tau)P_2(\varepsilon) = \frac{1}{2\pi i}\int_C \exp(\gamma\tau)(\gamma - \varepsilon A - B)^{-1}d\gamma$

$$= \sum_{k=0}^{\infty} \varepsilon^k \frac{1}{2\pi i}\int_C \exp(\gamma\tau)[(\gamma - B)^{-1}A]^k(\gamma - B)^{-1}d\gamma.$$

Thus

$$Y_k(\tau) = \frac{1}{2\pi i}\int_C \exp(\gamma\tau)[(\gamma - B)^{-1}A]^k(\gamma - B)^{-1}d\gamma, \qquad (18)$$

C a contour around the nonzero eigenvalues of B but not including zero, and hence

$$Y_k(0) = \frac{1}{2\pi i}\int_C [(\gamma - B)^{-1}A]^k(\gamma - B)^{-1}d\gamma. \qquad (19)$$

In particular, $Y_o(0) = BB^D$ and $Y_o(\tau) = \exp(B\tau)BB^D$. One cannot get a formula similar to (18) for $X_k(t)$ which does not have an ε in the exponential.

If B is stable, then $X_k(t) = 0$ for all $k \geq 0$ and $B^D = B^{-1}$, so that our results reduce to the known results. We summarize our results as follows.

Theorem 5.3.1 Let $X_\varepsilon(t) = \exp((A + B/\varepsilon)t)$. Then $X_\varepsilon(t)$ has an asymptotic expansion for $t \geq 0$ if and only if B is semistable. Suppose B is semistable. Then with $\tau = t/\varepsilon$

$$X_\varepsilon(t) = \sum_{k=0}^{\infty} \varepsilon^k X_k(t) + \sum_{k=0}^{\infty} \varepsilon^k Y_k(\tau),$$

and both series converge for all $t \geq 0$ for small enough ε. The $X_k(t)$ are given by (3), (11), (12) and the $Y_k(\tau)$ by (17) or (18) and (19).

4. $e^{(A + B/\varepsilon)t}$; NONCONSTANT A,B

While A,B were assumed constant for notational convenience in Sections 2 and 3, the following more general theorem holds.

Theorem 5.4.1 Suppose that $A(\varepsilon) \to A_o$ as $\varepsilon \to 0^+$. Suppose that $B(\varepsilon)$ is right differentiable at $\varepsilon = 0$. Let $X_\varepsilon(t) = e^{(A(\varepsilon) + B(\varepsilon)/\varepsilon)t}$. Then $X_\varepsilon(t)$ converges pointwise for $0 < t < t_o$ if and only if $B(0)$ is semistable. If $B(0)$ is semistable, then

(i) $\lim_{\varepsilon \to 0^+} X_\varepsilon(t) = e^{[A_o + \dot{B}(0);B(0)]t}[I;B(0)]$,

(ii) $X_\varepsilon(t)$ converges uniformly on compact subsets of $(0,\infty)$,

(iii) $\dot{X}_\varepsilon(t)$ converges uniformly on compact subsets of $(0,\infty)$ to

$$[A_o + \dot{B}(0);B(0)]e^{[A_o + \dot{B}(0);B(0)]t}[I;B(0)].$$

Proof It is clear from the proof of Theorem 2.1 that it goes over immediately to $A(\varepsilon) \to A_o$. Suppose then that $B(\varepsilon)$ is differentiable at $\varepsilon = 0$. Thus $B(\varepsilon) = B(0) + \dot{B}(0)\varepsilon + \phi(\varepsilon)$ where $\phi(\varepsilon)/\varepsilon \to 0$ as $\varepsilon \to 0^+$. Then,

$A(\varepsilon) + B(\varepsilon)/\varepsilon = [A(\varepsilon) + \dot{B}(0) + \phi(\varepsilon)/\varepsilon] + B(0)/\varepsilon$ and $A(\varepsilon) + \dot{B}(0) + \phi(\varepsilon)/\varepsilon \to A_o + \dot{B}(0)$ which is the case just discussed. There remains then only to verify (ii) and (iii). But if $B(0)$ is semistable, then, $X_\varepsilon(t) = e^{F_0(\varepsilon)t} P_0(\varepsilon) + e^{F_1(\varepsilon)t} P_1(\varepsilon)$ where $\mathrm{Re}[\sigma(F_1(\varepsilon))\setminus\{0\}] < 0$ and $F_0(\varepsilon) \to [A_o + \dot{B}(0);B(0)]$. Since $\|e^{F_1(\varepsilon)t} P_1(\varepsilon)\| = O(e^{-Bt/\varepsilon})$ by (2.18), both (ii) and (iii) follow. □

If A,B are analytic in ε, the approach of Section 3 is easily modified to compute the exponential's expansion. First observe that $A(\varepsilon) + B(\varepsilon)/\varepsilon$ is of the form $\tilde{A}(\varepsilon) + B(0)/\varepsilon$ where $\tilde{A}$ is analytic at zero. Thus we may suppose A is analytic in ε and B is constant. Then Section 3 is modified as follows.

If $A(\varepsilon) = \sum_{i=0}^{\infty} A_i\varepsilon^i$, then in (3), A is replaced by A_o and (3.7:k) is

$$BX_{k+1} + A_oX_k + A_1X_{k-1} + \ldots + A_kX_o = \dot{X}_k, \quad k \geq 0. \tag{1:k}$$

(1:k) of course determines B^DBX_{k+1} in terms of the lower X_k, while $[I;B]X_{k+1}$ is found by solving the differential equation obtained by multiplying (1:k+1) by $[I;B]$.

One may also get a formula like (16) but the ε power series for $\sum_{k=0}^{\infty} [(\gamma - B)^{-1}A(\varepsilon)]^k(\gamma - B)^{-1}\varepsilon^k$ must be computed, which is straightforward. The same holds for the analogue of (17).

Thus we would get, for example, that

$$X_o(0) = I - B^DB = [I;B],$$

$$X_1(0) = \frac{1}{2\pi i}\int_C (I + (\gamma - B)^{-1}A_o)(\gamma - B)^{-1}d\gamma, \text{ and}$$

$$X_2(0) = \frac{1}{2\pi i}\int_C [I + (\gamma-B)^{-1}A_1 + \sum_{r=0}^{2} (\gamma-B)^{-1}A_r(\gamma-B)^{-1}A_{2-r}](\gamma-B)^{-1}d\gamma.$$

The above integrals are easily evaluated as in the proof of Proposition 3.1.

5. ADDITIONAL POWERS OF ε; EXISTENCE OF LIMITS

In this section we shall be concerned with the existence and calculation of limits of

$$X_\varepsilon(t) = e^{(A(\varepsilon) + B/\varepsilon + C/\varepsilon^r + E/\varepsilon^s)t} \tag{1}$$

where $s > r > 1$, $A(\varepsilon)$, B, C, E are $n \times n$ matrices, and $A(\varepsilon)$ is right continuous at zero.

Different powers of ε may occur explicitly in the formulation of the system. There is another way that they can occur. In Section 3 we considered the exponential

$$e^{(A(\varepsilon) + B(\varepsilon)/\varepsilon)t} \tag{2}$$

where the $A(\varepsilon)$ were right continuous at zero and the $B(\varepsilon)$ were right differentiable at zero. Suppose, however, that the $B(\varepsilon)$ were not right differentiable, but rather had a Taylor expansion in ε^r, $r < 1$. Say, $B(\varepsilon) = B(0) + B^{(1)}(0)\varepsilon^r + B^{(2)}(0)\varepsilon + O(\varepsilon)$. For example, $B(\varepsilon)$ might be satisfying a Lipschitz type of condition. Then (1) becomes for $\delta = \varepsilon^{1-r}$, $e^{(\tilde{A}(\delta) + B^{(1)}(0)\delta^{-1} + B_1(0)\delta^{-s})}$ where $s = (1 - r)^{-1} > 1$, and $A(\delta)$ is right continuous at $\delta = 0$.

Thus the results of this section may also be viewed as a direct extension of Sections 2 and 4.

We shall calculate (1) first in the case when $E = 0$. The $\mathrm{Ind}(E) = 1$ case will then be handled. The method for calculation with more powers of ε should then be clear.

It is not hard to see that if $\exp\left((\sum_{i=1}^{m} A_i \varepsilon^{-r_i}) t \right)$; $0 = r_1 < r_2 < .. < r_m$, has a pointwise limit for all $t > 0$, then $\mathrm{Re}\,\sigma(A_m) \leq 0$. However, if $m > 2$, then the semistability of A_m is no longer necessary or sufficient.

We begin with an important special case.

<u>The E = 0, C semistable case</u>

<u>Theorem 5.5.1</u> Suppose $\mathrm{Ind}(C) = 1$ and C is semistable. Let

$$X_\varepsilon(t) = e^{(A + B/\varepsilon + C/\varepsilon^r)t}, \quad r > 1. \tag{3}$$

Then (3) converges for an $r \geq 2$, for all $t > 0$, if and only if $[B;C]$ is semistable. Suppose $[B;C]$ is semistable.

(i) If $r > 2$, then (3) converges to

$$e^{[[A;C];[B;C]]t}(I - [B;C]^D[B;C])(I - C^D C), \tag{4}$$

(ii) If $r = 2$, then the limit of (3) is the same as (4) except a term

$$-[[BC^D B;C];\ [B;C]]t \tag{5}$$

is added into the exponential.

<u>Proof</u> Since the first part of the proof is like that of Theorem 2.1, we shall omit some technical details. Suppose C is semistable. Then $\sigma(A + B/\varepsilon + C/\varepsilon^r)$ is contained in the union of two disjoint open sets $Q_1(\varepsilon)$, $Q_2(\varepsilon)$; $\mathrm{Sup}\,\{\mathrm{Re}\lambda \mid \lambda \in Q_1(\varepsilon)\} \leq Me^{-1/\varepsilon^r}$ and $Q_2(\varepsilon)$ contains zero and grows as $O(1/\varepsilon)$. Let C_1, C_2 be contours (depending on ε) around $Q_1(\varepsilon)$, $Q_2(\varepsilon)$. Let

$$P_i(\varepsilon) = \frac{1}{2\pi i} \int_{C_i} (\lambda - A - B/\varepsilon - C/\varepsilon^r)^{-1} d\lambda, \tag{6}$$

and

$$F_i(\varepsilon) = \frac{1}{2\pi i}\int_{C_i} \lambda(\lambda - A - B/\varepsilon - C/\varepsilon^r)^{-1}d\lambda. \tag{7}$$

Then $P_i(\varepsilon) = \frac{1}{2\pi i}\int_{\hat{C}_i} (\gamma - \varepsilon^r A - \varepsilon^{r-1}B - C)^{-1}d\gamma$, $\gamma = \lambda\varepsilon^r$. Hence,

$P_i(\varepsilon) \to \frac{1}{2\pi i}\int_{\hat{C}_i} (\gamma - C)^{-1}d\gamma$ so that $P_1(\varepsilon) \to CC^D$, $P_2(\varepsilon) \to I - CC^D$, since $\mathrm{Ind}(C) = 1$. Also, $e^{(A + B/\varepsilon + C/\varepsilon^r)t} = e^{F_1(\varepsilon)t}P_1(\varepsilon) + e^{F_2(\varepsilon)t}P_2(\varepsilon)$. Since $e^{F_1(\varepsilon)t}P_1(\varepsilon) \to 0$, it suffices to compute the limit of $e^{F_2(\varepsilon)t}$. We shall not worry about the γ-contour around zero but note that once ε is taken small enough, the contour may be taken independent of ε. The specific contour will be omitted in what follows. We shall make frequent use of the identity

$$(\mu - X - Y)^{-1} = (\mu - X - Y)^{-1}X(\mu - Y)^{-1} + (\mu - Y)^{-1} \tag{8}$$

which holds if $\mu - X - Y$ and $\mu - Y$ are invertible.

Now by (8) $F_2(\varepsilon) = \frac{1}{2\pi i}\int_C \frac{\gamma}{\varepsilon^r}(\gamma - \varepsilon^r A - \varepsilon^{r-1}B - C)^{-1}d\gamma$

$$= \frac{1}{2\pi i}\int_C \gamma[(\gamma - \varepsilon^r A - \varepsilon^{r-1}B - C)^{-1}A(\gamma - \varepsilon^{r-1}B - C)^{-1}]d\gamma \tag{9}$$

$$+ \frac{1}{2\pi i}\int_C \frac{\gamma}{\varepsilon^r}(\gamma - \varepsilon^{r-1}B - C)^{-1}d\gamma. \tag{10}$$

We first compute (10); using (8) twice; $\frac{1}{2\pi i}\int_C \frac{\gamma}{\varepsilon^r}(\gamma - \varepsilon^{r-1}B - C)^{-1}d\gamma$

$$= \frac{1}{2\pi i}\int_C \frac{\gamma}{\varepsilon}(\gamma - \varepsilon^{r-1}B - C)^{-1}B(\gamma - C)^{-1}d\gamma + 0$$

$$= \frac{1}{2\pi i}\int_C \frac{\gamma}{\varepsilon}[(\gamma - \varepsilon^{r-1}B - C)^{-1}\varepsilon^{r-1}B(\gamma - C)^{-1} + (\gamma - C)^{-1}]B(\gamma - C)^{-1}d\gamma$$

$$= \frac{1}{2\pi i}\int_C \gamma(\gamma - \varepsilon^{r-1}B - C)^{-1}\varepsilon^{r-2}[B(\gamma - C)^{-1}]^2 d\gamma$$

$$+ \frac{1}{\varepsilon}\frac{1}{2\pi i}\int_C \gamma(\gamma - C)^{-1}B(\gamma - C)^{-1}d\gamma.$$

Thus from (9), (10), and Proposition 3.1, we have for $r = 2$;

$$F_2(\varepsilon) = O(\varepsilon) + [A;C] + \frac{1}{2\pi i}\int \gamma(\gamma - C)^{-1}[B(\gamma - C)^{-1}]^2 d\gamma + [B;C]/\varepsilon. \quad (11)$$

If $r > 2$, we have

$$F_2(\varepsilon) = O(\varepsilon) + (I - C^DC)A(I - C^DC) + (I - C^DC)B(I - C^DC)/\varepsilon. \quad (12)$$

Applying Theorem 2.1 gives (4) from (11). To see (5), use Proposition 3.2, Theorem 2.1 and observe that

$$-\begin{bmatrix} I & 0 \\ 0 & [I;B_{22}] \end{bmatrix}\begin{bmatrix} 0 & \hat{C}^{-1}B_{12}B_{22} \\ B_{22}B_{21}\hat{C}^{-1} & B_{21}\hat{C}^{-1}B_{12} \end{bmatrix}\begin{bmatrix} I & 0 \\ 0 & [I;B_{22}] \end{bmatrix}$$

$$= -\begin{bmatrix} 0 & 0 \\ 0 & [B_{21}\hat{C}^{-1}B_{12};B_{22}] \end{bmatrix}$$

$$= -\begin{bmatrix} I & 0 \\ 0 & [I;B_{22}] \end{bmatrix}\begin{bmatrix} 0 & 0 \\ B_{21} & 0 \end{bmatrix}\begin{bmatrix} \hat{C}^{-1} & 0 \\ 0 & 0 \end{bmatrix}\begin{bmatrix} 0 & B_{12} \\ 0 & 0 \end{bmatrix}\begin{bmatrix} I & 0 \\ 0 & [I;B_{22}] \end{bmatrix}. \quad \square$$

If $r < 2$, then (3) may diverge.

Example 5.5.1 Let $A = 0$, $B = \begin{bmatrix} 0 & 1 \\ 2 & 0 \end{bmatrix}$, $C = \begin{bmatrix} -2 & 0 \\ 0 & 0 \end{bmatrix}$, and consider (3). Then C and [B;C] are both semistable. But (3) will only have a limit for $r \geq 2$. For $0 < r < 2$, $B/\varepsilon + C/\varepsilon^r$ has an eigenvalue $\lambda(\varepsilon)$ such that $\mathrm{Re}\lambda(\varepsilon) \to \infty$. Note that in this example, (5) is nonzero.

The E semistable case

By taking $B = 0$, Example 1 shows that (2) can diverge if $2r > s$. Accordingly, we shall take $r \geq 2$, $s \geq 2r$. Assume E is semistable. As before it suffices to evaluate the following contour integral around zero. Let $\gamma = \varepsilon^s\lambda$. Then by (8), $\frac{1}{2\pi i}\int_C \lambda(\lambda - A - B/\varepsilon - C/\varepsilon^r - E/\varepsilon^s)^{-1}d\lambda$

$$= \frac{1}{2\pi i}\int_C \frac{\gamma}{\varepsilon^s}[(\gamma - \varepsilon^s A - B\varepsilon^{s-1} - C\varepsilon^{s-r} - E)^{-1}\varepsilon^s A(\gamma - B\varepsilon^{s-1} - C\varepsilon^{s-r} - E)^{-1}$$

$$+ (\gamma - \varepsilon^{s-1}B - \varepsilon^{s-r}C - E)^{-1}]d\gamma$$

$$= \frac{1}{2\pi i}\int_C \frac{\gamma}{\varepsilon^s}(\gamma - \varepsilon^{s-1}B - \varepsilon^{s-r}C - E)^{-1}d\gamma + [A;E] + O(\varepsilon). \tag{13}$$

Now again by (8),

$$\frac{1}{2\pi i}\int \frac{\gamma}{\varepsilon^s}(\gamma - \varepsilon^{s-1}B - \varepsilon^{s-r}C - E)^{-1}d\gamma$$

$$= \begin{cases} \frac{1}{2\pi i}\int \frac{\gamma}{\varepsilon}(\gamma - \varepsilon^{s-1}B - \varepsilon^{s-r}C - E)^{-1}B(\gamma - \varepsilon^{s-r}C - E)^{-1}d\gamma & (14) \\ + \frac{1}{2\pi i}\int \frac{\gamma}{\varepsilon^s}(\gamma - \varepsilon^{s-r}C - E)^{-1}d\gamma. & (15) \end{cases}$$

We shall compute (14) and (15). By (8), (15) is

$$
= \begin{cases} \dfrac{\varepsilon^{s-2}}{2\pi i} \displaystyle\int_C \gamma(\gamma - \varepsilon^{s-1}B - \varepsilon^{s-r}C - E)^{-1}[B(\gamma - \varepsilon^{s-r}C - E)^{-1}]^2 d\gamma & (16) \\ + \dfrac{1}{2\pi i} \displaystyle\int_C \dfrac{\gamma}{\varepsilon} (\gamma - \varepsilon^{s-r}C - E)^{-1}B(\gamma - \varepsilon^{s-r}C - E)^{-1}d\gamma. & (17) \end{cases}
$$

The integral (16) will not matter since $s > 2$. (17) then becomes

$$
\frac{1}{2\pi i} \int_C \frac{\gamma}{\varepsilon} [(\gamma - \varepsilon^{s-r}C - E)^{-1}\varepsilon^{s-r}C(\gamma - E)^{-1} + (\gamma - E)^{-1}]B \cdot
$$

$$
[(\gamma - \varepsilon^{s-r}C - E)^{-1}\varepsilon^{s-r}C(\gamma - E)^{-1} + (\gamma - E)^{-1}]d\gamma
$$

$$
= \begin{cases} \dfrac{1}{2\pi i} \displaystyle\int_C \dfrac{\gamma}{\varepsilon} (\gamma - E)^{-1}B(\gamma - E)^{-1}d\gamma & (18) \\ + \dfrac{\varepsilon^{s-r-1}}{2\pi i} \displaystyle\int_C \gamma(\gamma - \varepsilon^{s-r}C - E)^{-1}C(\gamma - E)^{-1}B(\gamma - E)^{-1}d\gamma & (19) \\ + \dfrac{\varepsilon^{s-r-1}}{2\pi i} \displaystyle\int_C \gamma(\gamma - E)^{-1}B(\gamma - \varepsilon^{s-r}C - E)^{-1}C(\gamma - E)^{-1}d\gamma & (20) \\ + \dfrac{\varepsilon^{2s-2r-1}}{2\pi i} \displaystyle\int_C \gamma(\gamma-\varepsilon^{s-r}C-E)^{-1}C(\gamma-E)^{-1}B(\gamma-\varepsilon^{s-r}C-E)^{-1}C(\gamma- E)^{-1}d\gamma. & (21) \end{cases}
$$

Now (15) is

$$
\frac{1}{2\pi i} \int_C \frac{\gamma}{\varepsilon^s} [(\gamma - \varepsilon^{s-r}C - E)^{-1}\varepsilon^{s-r}C(\gamma - E)^{-1} + (\gamma - E)^{-1}]d\gamma
$$

$$
= \frac{1}{2\pi i} \int_C \frac{\gamma}{\varepsilon^r} (\gamma - \varepsilon^{s-r}C - E)^{-1}C(\gamma - E)^{-1}d\gamma
$$

$$= \frac{1}{2\pi i} \int_C \gamma\varepsilon^{s-2r} (\gamma - \varepsilon^{s-r}C - E)^{-1}[C(\gamma - E)^{-1}]^2 d\gamma$$

$$+ \frac{1}{2\pi i} \int_C \frac{1}{\varepsilon^r} \gamma(\gamma - E)^{-1}C(\gamma - E)^{-1}d\gamma. \tag{22}$$

Observe that (18), (19), (20), (21) go to zero in ε, so that combining (15) - (21) gives $F_2(\varepsilon)$ is

$$O(\varepsilon) + [A;E] + \frac{\varepsilon^{s-2r}}{2\pi i} \int_C \gamma(\gamma-E)^{-1}[C(\gamma-E)^{-1}]^2 d\gamma + \frac{1}{\varepsilon} [B;E] + \frac{1}{\varepsilon^r} [C;E]. \tag{23}$$

Theorem 1 can now be applied to (23) to yield the following result.

<u>Theorem 5.5.1</u> Suppose that E is semistable. Suppose also that [C;E] is semistable. Then $e^{(A + B/\varepsilon + C/\varepsilon^r + E/\varepsilon^s)t}$ converges pointwise for all $t > 0$ if and only if [[B;E]; [C;E]] is semistable. Suppose [[B;E]; [C;E]] is semistable.

(i) If $s > 2r$, $r > 2$, the limit is

$$e^{[[A;E];\ [C;E]];\ [[B;E];\ [C;E]]]t}Q \tag{24}$$

where $Q = [I;[[B;E];\ [C;E]]][I;[C;E]][I;E]$.

(ii) If $s > 2r$, $r = 2$, the limit is the same as (24) except a term

$$[[[B;E][C;E]^D[B;E];\ [C;E]];\ [B;E]]t \tag{25}$$

is added into the exponential (24).

(iii) If $s = 2r$, $r > 2$, the limit is the same as (24) except the term

$[EC^DE;E]t$ is added into the exponential (24). (26)

(iv) If $s = 2r = 4$, then both (25) and (26) are added into the exponential in (24).

E = 0, C not semistable

From Theorems 2.1, 1 and 2, the pattern that the limit follows for additional powers of ε should be clear. We now turn to examine what happens if the leading coefficient A_m has purely imaginary eigenvalues or does not have Index 1. Intuitively, one might expect that some A_r will have to dampen the resulting oscillations. For simplicity of exposition we shall examine the $E = 0$ case since as Theorems 1 and 2 show the $E \neq 0$ case often gives insight into the $E = 0$ case.

The first thing to notice is that even if B is stable and $\mathrm{Re}\sigma(C) \leq 0$, then (2) may not have a pointwise limit as the following Example shows.

Example 5.5.2 Let $A = 0$, $B = \begin{bmatrix} -1 & 0 \\ 1 & -2 \end{bmatrix}$, $C = \begin{bmatrix} 0 & 1 \\ 0 & 0 \end{bmatrix}$, and consider $\exp((B/\varepsilon + C/\varepsilon^r)t) = Z_\varepsilon(t)$, where $r > 1$. Then $Z_\varepsilon(t)$ fails to converge as $\varepsilon \to 0^+$ for all $t > 0$ since $B/\varepsilon + C/_\varepsilon r$ has an eigenvalue λ_ε such that $\mathrm{Re}\lambda_\varepsilon \to +\infty$.

Of course, this example shows that in general a complex eigenvalue α of C cannot be dampened out by B if $\mathrm{Ind}(\alpha - C) > 1$. However, even if $\mathrm{Ind}(\alpha - C) \leq 1$, then a stable B may not be able to dampen out the oscillations. To see exactly what the sufficient conditions are, suppose that $\mathrm{Re}\sigma(C) \leq 0$ and $\mathrm{Ind}(\alpha - C) = 1$ for all $\alpha \in \sigma(C)$ such that $\mathrm{Re}\alpha = 0$. By the same arguments as used in Theorems 1, 2, it suffices to characterize when $e^{F(\varepsilon)t}$ has a limit where

$$F(\varepsilon) = \frac{1}{2\pi i} \int_{\mathcal{C}} \lambda(\lambda - (A + B/\varepsilon + C/_\varepsilon r))^{-1} d\lambda, \tag{27}$$

$\mathcal{C}$ a contour around $\alpha\varepsilon^{-r}$ whose interior is disjoint from the interior of the contours around the other purely imaginary eigenvalues and the eigenvalues of negative real part. Note that the contours' centers move apart as ε^{-r} while their diameters grow as ε^{-1}.

Now let $s = (\lambda - \alpha\varepsilon^{-r})\varepsilon^{r}$. Then (27) becomes

$$F(\varepsilon) = \frac{1}{2\pi i} \int_{\hat{C}} \frac{(s+\alpha)}{\varepsilon^{r}} (s - (\varepsilon^{r} A + \varepsilon^{r-1} B + C))^{-1} ds, \tag{28}$$

$\hat{C}$ is a contour around zero. Let $C_\alpha = C - \alpha$. Then

$$\begin{aligned} F(\varepsilon) &= \frac{1}{2\pi i} \int_{\hat{C}} (s + \alpha)(s - C_\alpha)^{-1} A (s - C_\alpha)^{-1} ds \\ &+ \frac{\varepsilon^{r-2}}{2\pi i} \int_{\hat{C}} (s + \alpha)(s - C_\alpha)^{-1} B (s - C_\alpha)^{-1} B (s - C_\alpha)^{-1} ds \\ &+ \frac{1}{\varepsilon 2\pi i} \int_{\hat{C}} (s + \alpha)(s - C_\alpha)^{-1} B (s - C_\alpha)^{-1} ds + O(\varepsilon). \end{aligned} \tag{29}$$

If $r \geq 2$, then $\exp(F(\varepsilon)t)$ will converge by Theorem 2.1 if and only if

$$B_\alpha = \frac{1}{2\pi i} \int_{\hat{C}} (s + \alpha)(s - C_\alpha)^{-1} B (s - C_\alpha)^{-1} ds \tag{30}$$

is semistable. But a slight modification of the proof of Proposition 3.1 gives

$$B_\alpha = [B;C_\alpha] - \alpha[I;C_\alpha]BC^{D} - \alpha C_\alpha^{D} B[I;C_\alpha]. \tag{31}$$

We summarize our discussion as follows.

<u>Theorem 5.5.3</u> Suppose that $\mathrm{Re}\,\sigma(C) \leq 0$. Let $\{\alpha_1, \ldots, \alpha_r\}$ be those $\alpha \in \sigma(C)$ such that $\mathrm{Re}\,\alpha = 0$. Assume that $\mathrm{Ind}(C - \alpha_i) = 1$ for $i = 1, \ldots, r$. Then for $r \geq 2$

$$X_\varepsilon(t) = e^{(A + B/\varepsilon + C/\varepsilon^{r})t} \tag{32}$$

converges pointwise for all $t > 0$ if and only if B_{α_i} defined by (31) is semistable for $i = 1,\ldots,r$. If the limit exists, it is given as follows;

(i) If $r > 2$, then the limit of (32) is

$$\sum_{i=1}^{r} e^{[A_{\alpha_i};B_{\alpha_i}]t}[I;B_{\alpha_i}][I;C_{\alpha_i}]. \tag{33}$$

(ii) If $r = 2$, then the term

$$\begin{aligned}&\{-[[B_\alpha C_\alpha^D B_\alpha;C_\alpha];\ [B_\alpha;C_\alpha]] + (C_\alpha^D B_\alpha[I;C_\alpha] + [I;C_\alpha]B_\alpha C_\alpha^D)B_\alpha C_\alpha^D \\ &+ (C_\alpha^D - [I;C_\alpha])B_\alpha C_\alpha^D B[I;C_\alpha]\}t\end{aligned} \tag{34}$$

is added into the $i^{\underline{th}}$ exponential in (33), where

$$A_\alpha = [A;C_\alpha] - \alpha(C_\alpha^D A[I;C_\alpha] + [I;C_\alpha]AC_\alpha^D). \tag{35}$$

Theorem 3 follows from (29) - (31) by Theorem 1 once the integrals are computed. We leave the proof to the interested reader. Details may be found in [8].

It should be noted that the stability of B in Theorem 3 is not enough to guarantee the semistability of B_α.

<u>Example 5.5.3</u> Let $C = \begin{bmatrix} 0 & 0 \\ 0 & -i \end{bmatrix}$, $B = \begin{bmatrix} -3 & -1 \\ 1 & 0 \end{bmatrix}$, $A = 0$. Then B is stable since both eigenvalues are negative real. Also B_α for $\alpha = 0$ is semistable since it is zero. But B_α for $\alpha = -i$ is $\begin{bmatrix} 0 & -1 \\ 1 & 0 \end{bmatrix}$ which is not semistable since $\pm\, i$ are its eigenvalues.

Note that in Theorem 1, 2, 3 one may repalce A by $A(\varepsilon)$ where $A(\varepsilon)$ is right continuous at zero. Then $A(0)$ replaces A in the limits.

6. ADDITIONAL POWERS OF ε; THE FULL EXPANSION

This section will discuss the asymptotic expansion of

$$\exp((A + B/\varepsilon + C/_{\varepsilon}r)t) \tag{1}$$

Necessarily we need that (1) have a limit as $\varepsilon \to 0^+$, $t > 0$. Various sufficient conditions are given in Section 5. We shall assume that C and [B;C] are semistable. Our approach can be modified to cover other sufficient cases. As observed in Section 5, the $r = 2$ case is slightly more complicated than the $r > 2$ case. Accordingly, we shall consider only the $r = 2$ case. The same approach works for larger r. As in the earlier sections, we may assume, without loss of generality, that B,C are constants. A is temporarily assumed constant.

From Section 5, (1) may be written as $\exp(F_1(\varepsilon)t)P_1(\varepsilon) + \exp(F_2(\varepsilon)t)P_2(\varepsilon)$ where $\exp(F_i(\varepsilon)t)P_1(\varepsilon)$, $i = 1,2$ satisfies

$$\frac{dZ}{dt} = (A + B/\varepsilon + C/\varepsilon^2)Z \tag{2}$$

Now $\varepsilon^2 F_1(\varepsilon)$ is analytic in ε since $F_1(\varepsilon) = \frac{1}{2\pi i}\int_C \gamma/\varepsilon^2(\gamma - \varepsilon^2 A - \varepsilon B - C)^{-1}d\gamma$

C a contour around $\sigma(C)\setminus\{0\}$ not including zero.

Let $\tau = t/\varepsilon^2$. Then

$$\exp(\varepsilon^2 F_1(\varepsilon)\tau)P_1(\varepsilon) = \sum_{n=0}^{\infty} Y_n(\tau)\varepsilon^n = \int_C \exp(\gamma\tau)(\gamma-\varepsilon^2A-\varepsilon B-C)^{-1}d\gamma. \tag{3}$$

The $Y_n(\tau)$ will be calculated shortly. From Section 5,

$$F_2(\varepsilon) = \tilde{A}(\varepsilon) + [B;C]/\varepsilon. \tag{4}$$

Note that [B;C] is semistable by assumption and the rest of $F_2(\varepsilon)$ is analytic in ε. Thus we are in the case covered by Theorem 3.1 and get that

$$\exp((A + B/\varepsilon + C/\varepsilon^2)t) = \sum_{n=0}^{\infty} X_n(t)\varepsilon^n + \sum_{n=0}^{\infty} Y_n(\tau)\varepsilon^n + \sum_{n=0}^{\infty} Z_n(\mathcal{t})\varepsilon^n, \quad (5)$$

$\tau = t/\varepsilon^2$, $\mathcal{t} = t/\varepsilon$, and all three series in (5) satisfy (2).

<u>The $Y_k(\tau)$ terms</u> We may rewrite (2), using $\tau = t/\varepsilon^2$ as $\frac{dZ}{d\tau} = (\varepsilon^2 A + \varepsilon B + C)Z$. Substitution of $\sum_{k=0}^{\infty} Y_k(\tau)\varepsilon^k$ gives

$$\dot{Y}_0(\tau) = CY_0(\tau)$$

$$\dot{Y}_1(\tau) = CY_1(\tau) + BY_0(\tau) \quad (6)$$

$$\dot{Y}_k(\tau) = CY_k(\tau) + BY_{k-1}(\tau) + AY_{k-2}(\tau), \quad k \geq 2.$$

The equations (6) are easily solved to give $Y_k(\tau)$ recursively in terms of Y_{k-1} and Y_{k-2} once $Y_k(0)$ is known. Alternatively, note that

$$\sum_{k=0}^{\infty} \varepsilon^k Y_k(\tau) = \frac{1}{2\pi i} \int_C \exp(\gamma\tau)(\gamma - \varepsilon^2 A - \varepsilon B - C)^{-1} d\gamma$$

$$= \sum_{k=0}^{\infty} \varepsilon^k \frac{1}{2\pi i} \int_C \exp(\gamma\tau)[(\gamma - C)^{-1}(\varepsilon A + B)]^k (\gamma - C)^{-1} d\gamma.$$

By equating like powers of ε we get

$$Y_0(\tau) = \frac{1}{2\pi i} \int_C \exp(\gamma\tau)(\gamma - C)^{-1} d\gamma,$$

$$Y_1(\tau) = \frac{1}{2\pi i} \int_C \exp(\gamma\tau)[(\gamma - C)^{-1}B](\gamma - C)^{-1} d\gamma,$$

$$Y_2(\tau) = \frac{1}{2\pi i} \int_C \exp(\gamma\tau)[(\gamma - C)^{-1}A + [(\gamma - C)^{-1}B]^2(\gamma - C)^{-1}] d\gamma,$$

and so forth.

In particular, since $P_1(\varepsilon) = \sum_{m=0}^{\infty} Y_m(0)\varepsilon^m$, $Y_o(0) = C^D C$ and $Y_1(0) = -C^D B[I;C] - [I;C]BC^D$. Note that the Y_k terms for (1) and (3.1) do not differ in form until $k \geq 2$.

The $X_k(t)$ terms As with (3.1), the $Y_k(\tau)$ terms are fairly easily determined and the $X_k(t)$ terms are the more difficult. Substituting into (2) gives $(\varepsilon^2 A + \varepsilon B + C) \sum_{k=0}^{\infty} X_k(t)\varepsilon^k = \sum_{k=0}^{\infty} \dot{X}_k(t)\varepsilon^{k+2}$. That is,

$$CX_o = 0 \tag{7}$$

$$CX_1 + BX_o = 0 \tag{8}$$

$$CX_{k+2} + BX_{k+1} + AX_k = \dot{X}_1(t) \quad , \quad k \geq 0 \tag{9:k}$$

Note that the projection $[I;C]$ can be decomposed into two commutative projections as follows,

$$[I;C][B;C]^D[B;C] + [I;C][I;[B;C]]. \tag{10}$$

From Theorem 5.1,

$$X_o(t) = \exp(([[A;C];[B;C]] - [[BC^D B;C];[B;C]])t)[I;[B;C]][I;C]. \tag{11}$$

Suppose then that $X_i(t)$ is known for $0 \leq i \leq m - 1$. We will compute $X_m(t)$. From (8) and (9:m-2) we have

$$C^D CX_m = \begin{cases} -C^D BX_o & \text{if } m = 1 \qquad (12) \\ C^D \dot{X}_{m-2} - C^D BX_{m-1} - C^D AX_{m-2} & \text{if } m \geq 2. \qquad (12{:}m) \end{cases}$$

Now from (8:m-1) we get $[I;C]BX_m + [I;C]AX_{m-1} = [I;C]\dot{X}_{m-1}$ so that $[I;C][C;B]X_m = [I;C]\dot{X}_{m-1} - [I;C]AX_{m-1} - [I;C]BC^D CX_m$. Hence

$$[I;C][C;B]^D[C;B]X_m = [C;B]^D\dot{X}_{m-1} - [C;B]^DAX_{m-1} - [C;B]^DBC^DCX_m. \quad (13)$$

Since C^DCX_m is given by (12), there remains only to compute $[I;C][I;[C;B]]X_m$. This term is somewhat harder to obtain. From (12:m),

$$[I;C]BX_{m+1} + [I;C]AX_m = [I;C]\dot{X}_m. \quad (14)$$

But $[I;C]BX_{m+1} = [I;C]B[I;C]X_{m+1} + [I;C]BC^DCX_{m+1}$, so that multiplying (14) by $[I;[C;B]]$ gives

$$[I;[C;B]][I;C]BC^DCX_{m+1} + [I;[C;B]][I;C]AX_m = [I;[C;B]][I;C]\dot{X}_m. \quad (15)$$

Using (12), (15) becomes

$$[I;[C;B]][I;C]\dot{X}_m = [I;[C;B]][I;C]AX_m + [I;[C;B]][I;C]BC^D\{\dot{X}_{m-1} - BX_m - AX_{m-1}\}. \quad (16)$$

For notational convenience let $W_m = [I;[C;B]][I;C]X_m$. Then (16) can be written as

$$\dot{W}_m = [I;[C;B]][I;C](A - BC^DB)W_m + [I;[C;B]][I;C]\{A[C^DCX_m + [C;B]^D[C;B][I;C]X_m + BC^D\dot{X}_{m-1} - BC^DAX_{m-1} - BC^DB[C^DCX_m + [C;B]^D[C;B][I;C]X_m]\}. \quad (17)$$

The quantity in the { } brackets in (17) is known since $X_o,\ldots,X_{m-1}$ are known by assumption, and C^DCX_m and $[C;B]^D[C;B][I;C]X_m$ are given by (12), (13), (17). Thus adding together (12), (13) and the solution of (17) gives the $X_m(t)$ provided one knows $X_m(0)$ for all m.

By definition, if $\gamma = \varepsilon\lambda$,

$$\sum_{m=0}^{\infty} X_m(0)\varepsilon^m = \frac{1}{2\pi i}\int_{C} (\lambda - \tilde{A}(\varepsilon) - [B;C]/\varepsilon)^{-1} d\lambda (I - P_1(\varepsilon))$$

$$= \sum_{m=0}^{\infty} \frac{1}{2\pi i}\int_{\hat{C}} [(\gamma - [B;C])^{-1}\tilde{A}(\varepsilon)]^m \varepsilon^m (\gamma - [B;C])^{-1} d\gamma (I - P_1(\varepsilon)). \tag{18}$$

where

$$\tilde{A}(\varepsilon) = \frac{1}{2\pi i}\int_{C} \gamma\,(\gamma - \varepsilon^2 A - \varepsilon B - C)^{-1} A(\gamma - \varepsilon B - C)^{-1} d\gamma$$

$$+ \frac{1}{2\pi i}\int_{C} \gamma\,(\gamma - \varepsilon B - C)^{-1}[B(\gamma - C)^{-1}]^2 d\gamma$$

C a contour including only the zero eigenvalue of C, $\hat{C}$ a contour including only the zero eigenvalue of [B;C]. While $C, \hat{C}$ come from different contours in terms of λ, after they are written in terms of γ, they may be taken as the same, and we shall do so. Let $\tilde{A}(\varepsilon) = \sum_{m=0}^{\infty} A_m \varepsilon^m$, and note that from Proposition 3.2, $A_0 = [A;C] - [BC^D B;C] - C^D A[B;C] - [A;C]BC^D$. The other A_m may be calculated in like manner. Thus from (18) we may compute the $X_m(0)$. For example,

$$X_0(0) = \frac{1}{2\pi i}\int_{C} (\gamma - [B;C])^{-1} d\gamma (I - P_1(0)) = [I;[B;C]][I;C]$$

and

$$X_1(0) = [I;[B;C]](C^D B[I;C] + [I;C]BC^D) + (-[B;C]^D \tilde{A}(0)[I;[B;C]] -$$

$$[I;[B;C]]\tilde{A}(0)[B;C]^D)C^D C$$

The $Z_k(t)$ terms

Now (2) may be rewritten as $\frac{dZ}{dt} = (\varepsilon^2 A + \varepsilon B + C)Z$. Inserting the series $\sum_{m=0}^{\infty} Z_m(t)\varepsilon^m$, gives

$$CZ_o(t) = 0 \tag{19}$$

$$\dot{Z}_o(t) = CZ_1(t) + BZ_o(t) \tag{20}$$

$$\dot{Z}_m(t) = CZ_{m+1}(t) + BZ_m(t) + AZ_{m-1}(t) \quad , \quad m \geq 1 \tag{21:m}$$

Note that $Z_o(0) = I - Y_o(0) - X_o(0)$ and $Z_m(0) = -Y_m(0) - X_m(0)$ for $m \geq 1$. Thus the $Z_m(0)$ are known. From (19) $C^DCZ_o = 0$. Thus Z_o is given by (20) as $([I;C]\dot{Z}_o) = [I;C]BZ_o = [B;C]([I;C]Z_o)$. Hence

$$Z_o(t) = \exp([B;C]t)[I;C]. \tag{22}$$

Now if $Z_m(t)$ is known for $m \leq n - 1$, then $C^DCZ_n(t) = C^D\dot{Z}_{n-1}(t) - C^DBZ_{n-1}(t) - C^DAZ_{n-2}(t)$ by (22:m-1) and $[I;C]Z_n(t)$ is given from (21:m) as the solution of

$$\begin{aligned}[[I;C]\dot{Z}_n(t)] &= [B;C][I;C]Z_n(t) + [I;C]BC^DCZ_n(t) \\ &+ [I;C]AZ_{n-1}(t).\end{aligned} \tag{23}$$

Note that to solve (23) one needs only have $[I;C]Z_n(0)$ and not $Z_n(0)$.

7. MORE GENERAL AUTONOMOUS SYSTEMS

The singularly perturbed differential equations of the preceding sections were all of the form

$$A(\varepsilon)\dot{\underline{x}} = C(\varepsilon)\underline{x} + \underline{f}. \tag{1}$$

It is possible to rewrite (1) as $\varepsilon^{E}\dot{\underline{x}} = \tilde{C}(\varepsilon)\underline{x} + \underline{f}(\varepsilon)$, where E is diagonal which is the type of problem studied in Section 6 [34, p. 75]. That method also required computation of certain series. We are interested in working directly with (1). To analyze (1) it is helpful to be able to work with the fundamental solution of $A(\varepsilon)\dot{\underline{x}} = C(\varepsilon)\underline{x}$. If $A(\varepsilon)$ is invertible for $\varepsilon > 0$, $\underline{x}_{\varepsilon}(t) = \exp(-A^{-1}(\varepsilon)C(\varepsilon)t)\underline{x}(o)$, $\varepsilon > 0$. If $A(\varepsilon)$ is singular, but $\lambda_{\varepsilon}A(\varepsilon) + C(\varepsilon)$ is invertible, $\underline{x}_{\varepsilon}(t) = \exp([(\lambda_{\varepsilon}A(\varepsilon) - C(\varepsilon))^{-1}A(\varepsilon)]^{D}$ $[(\lambda_{\varepsilon}A(\varepsilon) - C(\varepsilon))^{-1}A(\varepsilon)]t)[I;(\lambda_{\varepsilon}A(\varepsilon) - C(\varepsilon))^{-1}A(\varepsilon)]\underline{x}(o)$. There is a difficulty in working with these exponentials that did not arise before. We shall present a method for dealing with some of these difficulties by considering

$$(A + \varepsilon B)\dot{\underline{x}}(t) = C\underline{x}(t) + \underline{f}(t) \tag{2}$$

and the associated reduced problem

$$A\dot{\underline{x}} = C\underline{x} + \underline{f}. \tag{3}$$

We allow, A, B, and C to all be singular, though we require that $A + \varepsilon B$ be invertible for small nonzero ε. The equation (3) will have solutions uniquely determined by consistent initial conditions if and only if there is a λ such that $\lambda A + C$ is invertible. We will assume such a λ exists so that the solution of (3) is given by Theorem 3.3.1.

In analyzing (2) we shall work with

$$X_{\varepsilon}(t) = \exp((A + \varepsilon B)^{-1}Ct). \tag{2}$$

Let $\hat{A} = (\mu A + B)^{-1}A$, $\hat{B} = (\mu A + B)^{-1}B = I - \mu\hat{A}$, $\hat{C} = (\mu A + B)^{-1}C$ where μ is some scalar such that $(\mu A + B)$ is invertible. Then

$$\exp((A + \varepsilon B)^{-1}Ct) = \exp((\hat{A} + \varepsilon\hat{B})^{-1}\hat{C}t). \tag{5}$$

From Theorem 4.2.1

$$(\hat{A}+\varepsilon\hat{B})^{-1} = \sum_{m=0}^{\infty} (-1)^m (\hat{A}^D\hat{B})^m \hat{A}^D \varepsilon^m + \hat{B}^D(I - \hat{A}\hat{A}^D) \sum_{m=0}^{k-1} (-1)^m (\hat{A}\hat{B}^D)^m \varepsilon^{-m-1} \tag{6}$$

where $k = \text{Ind}(\hat{A})$ for $0 < |\varepsilon| < r$, some $r > 0$. Thus (5) could be written as

$$\exp\left(\left(\sum_{i=1}^{\ell} A_i \varepsilon^{-r_i} + A_0(\varepsilon)\right)t\right) \quad , \quad 0 = r_0 < \ldots < r_\ell \tag{7}$$

If $[I;\hat{A}]\hat{A}^m\hat{B}^D\hat{C} = 0$ for $m \geq 1$ (or $m \geq 2$), then $\ell = 1$ ($\ell = 2$) and the expansion of (7) has been worked out in the earlier sections. However, in general, that approach becomes far too messy, so that we shall work with (5) directly though (6), (7) will be useful. We shall also see that the determination of the coefficients in the expansions necessitates working with an infinite, rather than finite system.

We shall assume that one has determined that (5) has a limit as $\varepsilon \to 0^+$ for $t \geq 0$. Our first goal is to write down an expansion. The second is to compute it.

<u>Proposition 5.7.1</u> Suppose that $G(\varepsilon)$ is an analytic matrix valued function for $0 < |\varepsilon| < \varepsilon_0$, some $\varepsilon_0 > 0$ and that $\exp(G(\varepsilon)t)$ has a limit as $\varepsilon \to 0^+$ for all $t > 0$. Then $G(\varepsilon) = G_1(\varepsilon) + G_2(\varepsilon)$, $\varepsilon > 0$, where $G_1(\varepsilon)G_2(\varepsilon) = G_2(\varepsilon)G_1(\varepsilon) = 0$, $\sigma(G(\varepsilon)) = \sigma(G_1(\varepsilon)) \cup \sigma(G_2(\varepsilon))$, $\sigma(G_1(\varepsilon))$ is bounded as $\varepsilon \to 0^+$, and $\max\{\text{Re}\lambda : \lambda \neq 0, \lambda \in \sigma(G_2(\varepsilon))\} \to -\infty$ as $\varepsilon \to 0^+$.

<u>Proof</u> We first show that $\exp(G(\varepsilon)t)$ has a limit as $\varepsilon \to 0^+$ for all $t > 0$, then $\sigma(G(\varepsilon)) \subseteq S_1(\varepsilon) \cup S_2(\varepsilon)$ where $S_1(\varepsilon)$ is bounded independent of ε and $\text{Re}S_2(\varepsilon) \to -\infty$. If this assertion is false, there exists $\varepsilon_i \to 0^+, \lambda(\varepsilon_i) \in \sigma(G(\varepsilon_i))$ such that $|\lambda(\varepsilon_i)| \to +\infty$ and $\text{Re}\lambda(\varepsilon_i) \geq M > -\infty$. Let $\underline{\phi}(\varepsilon_i)$ be an associated eigenvector of norm one. Taking a subsequence $\underline{\phi}(\varepsilon_j)$ such that $\underline{\phi}(\varepsilon_j)$ converges, we get a contradiction of the fact that

$\exp(G(\varepsilon_j)t)\underline{\phi}(\varepsilon_j) = \exp(\lambda(\varepsilon_j)t)\underline{\phi}(\varepsilon_j)$ has a limit for all $t > 0$. Thus $\sigma(G(\varepsilon)) \subseteq S_1(\varepsilon) \cup S_2(\varepsilon)$ where $S_1(\varepsilon)$ is bounded independent of ε and $\mathrm{Re}S_2(\varepsilon) \to -\infty$.

Now let $C_1(\varepsilon)$ be a contour around $S_1(\varepsilon) \cup \{\lambda | (\lambda A - C) \text{ is singular}\}$ and $C_2(\varepsilon)$ a contour around $S_2(\varepsilon)$, $\mathrm{Re}C_2(\varepsilon) \to -\infty$, such that their interiors do not intersect. Such contours exist for ε sufficiently small. One may assume $C_1(\varepsilon)$ is independent of ε.

Define $G_j(\varepsilon) = \frac{1}{2\pi i} \int_{C_j(\varepsilon)} \gamma(\gamma - (A + \varepsilon B)^{-1}C)^{-1} d\gamma.$

That the $G_j(\varepsilon)$ have the desired properties follows immediately from the functional calculus. $\square$

Let $P_j(\varepsilon) = \frac{1}{2\pi i} \int_{C_j(\varepsilon)} (\gamma - (A + \varepsilon B)^{-1}C)^{-1} d\gamma$. The $P_j(\varepsilon)$, $j = 1,2$ are commuting projections such that $P_1(\varepsilon)P_2(\varepsilon) = 0$, $P_1(\varepsilon) + P_2(\varepsilon) = I$. Now

$$P_1(\varepsilon) = \frac{1}{2\pi i} \int_{C_1} (\gamma(A + \varepsilon B) - C)^{-1}(A + \varepsilon B)d\gamma$$

$$= \frac{1}{2\pi i} \sum_{m=0}^{\infty} [-(\gamma A - C)^{-1}B]^m \varepsilon^m (\gamma A - C)^{-1}(A + \varepsilon B)d\gamma.$$

Hence $P_1(\varepsilon) = \sum_{m=0}^{\infty} Q_m \varepsilon^m$, where $Q_0 = \frac{1}{2\pi i} \int_{C_1} (\gamma A - C)^{-1} A d\gamma$ and for $m > 0$,

$$Q_m = \frac{1}{2\pi i} \int_{C_1} [-(\gamma A\text{-}C)^{-1}B]^m (\gamma A\text{-}C)^{-1}A + [-(\gamma A\text{-}C)^{-1}B]^{m-1}(\gamma A\text{-}C)^{-1}B d\gamma.$$

Since $P_1(\varepsilon) + P_2(\varepsilon) = I$, $P_2(\varepsilon) = \sum_{m=1}^{\infty} -Q_m\varepsilon^m + (I - Q_0)$. We shall compute Q_0. Let $\tilde{A} = (\lambda A - C)^{-1}A$, $\tilde{B} = (\lambda A - C)^{-1}B$, $\tilde{C} = (\lambda A - C)^{-1}C$, so that $\lambda\tilde{A} - \tilde{C} = I$.

Then $P_1(0) = Q_o = \frac{1}{2\pi i} \int_{C_1} (\gamma\tilde{A} - \tilde{C})^{-1}\tilde{A}d\gamma = \tilde{A}^D\tilde{A}$. Now let

$X(\varepsilon,t) = \exp(G_1(\varepsilon)t)P_1(\varepsilon)$. Clearly X is analytic in ε for some $|\varepsilon| \leq r$ so

$$X(\varepsilon,t) = \sum_{m=0}^{\infty} X_m(t)\varepsilon^m. \tag{8}$$

Let

$$\ell = 1 + \max\{m \mid (I - \hat{A}\hat{A}^D)\hat{A}^m\hat{B}^D\hat{C} \neq 0\}. \tag{9}$$

Then if $\tau = t/\varepsilon^\ell$, $\exp(\varepsilon^\ell(A + \varepsilon B)^{-1}C\tau)$ is analytic in ε by (5), (6) for $|\varepsilon| <$ some ε_o. Thus $Y(\varepsilon,\tau) = \exp(\varepsilon^\ell(A + \varepsilon B)^{-1}C\tau)P_2(\varepsilon)$ is analytic in ε so that

$$Y(\varepsilon,\tau) = \sum_{m=0}^{\infty} Y_m(\tau)\varepsilon^m \tag{10}$$

Note that the series (8), (10) both converge for $|\varepsilon|$ small, both satisfy the differential equation,

$$(A + \varepsilon B)\dot{Z} = CZ \tag{11}$$

and $X(\varepsilon,0) = P_1(\varepsilon)$, $Y(\varepsilon,0) = P_2(\varepsilon)$, so that

$$X_m(0) = Q_m \text{ for } m \geq 0,\ Y_m(0) = -Q_m \text{ for } m \geq 1, \text{ while } Y_o(0) = I - Q_o. \tag{12}$$

<u>Computation of the $X_m(t)$</u> Since $X(\varepsilon,t)$ satisfies (11), equating powers of ε gives,

$$A\dot{X}_o = CX_o \tag{13}$$

$$A\dot{X}_m = CX_m - B\dot{X}_{m-1}, \text{ for } m \geq 1. \tag{14.m}$$

Now A is allowed to be singular so that (13) and (14.m) are both singular differential equations. They will uniquely determine solutions precisely when there is a λ such that $\lambda A - C$ is invertible. From Theorem 3.3.1 we have the following:

Theorem 5.7.1 The coefficients $X_m(t)$ in (8) are given recursively by

$$X_o(t) = \exp(-\tilde{A}^D\tilde{C}t)\tilde{A}^D\tilde{A}X_o(0), \tag{15}$$

and for $m \geq 1$,

$$X_m(t) = \tilde{A}^D \exp(-\tilde{A}^D\tilde{C}t) \int_o^t \exp(\tilde{A}^D\tilde{C}s)(-\tilde{B}\dot{X}_{m-1}(s))ds$$
$$+ [I;\tilde{A}] \sum_{n=0}^{k-1} (-1)^n (\tilde{A}\tilde{C}^D)^n \tilde{C}^D X_{m-1}^{(n)}(t) + \exp(-\tilde{A}^D\tilde{C}t)\tilde{A}^D\tilde{A}X_m(0). \tag{16}$$

The $X_m(0)$ are given by (12), $k = \operatorname{Ind}(\tilde{A})$.

Computation of the $Y_m(\tau)$

The $Y_m(\tau)$ turn out to be harder to get than the $X_m(t)$. They are also not computable, or at least not obviously so, by the techniques of Section 3. Inserting (10) into (11) and equating coefficients, gives

$$A\dot{Y}_o(\tau) = 0 \tag{17.0}$$

$$A\dot{Y}_r(\tau) + B\dot{Y}_{r-1}(\tau) = 0 \quad , \quad 1 \leq r \leq \ell - 1 \tag{18.r-1}$$

$$A\dot{Y}_r(\tau) + B\dot{Y}_{r-1}(\tau) = CY_{r-\ell}(\tau) \quad , \quad \ell \leq r < \infty \tag{18.r}$$

Multiply every equation in (18) by $(\lambda A + B)^{-1}$ and write (17), (18) as

$$\mathcal{A}\underline{\dot{Y}}(\tau) = \mathcal{B}\underline{Y}(\tau). \tag{19}$$

If $\alpha = \{\alpha_i\}$ is a sequence of $n_i \times n_i$ matrices, let $S(\alpha) = S\{\alpha_1, \alpha_2, \dots\} = S\{\alpha_i\}$ be the striped matrix.

$$\begin{bmatrix} \alpha_1 & 0 & 0 & \cdot \\ \alpha_2 & \alpha_1 & 0 & \cdot \\ \alpha_3 & \alpha_2 & \alpha_1 & \cdot \\ \cdot & \cdot & \cdot & \cdot \end{bmatrix} \tag{20}$$

Then in (19) $\mathcal{A} = S\{\hat{A}, \hat{B}, 0, 0, \dots\}$, $\mathcal{B} = S\{\delta_{i,\ell+1}\hat{C}\}$, where $\delta_{i\ell} = 0$ if $i \neq \ell$, and $\delta_{i\ell} = 1$ if $i = \ell$ and $\underline{Y}(\tau) = \{Y_i(\tau)\}_{i=0}^{\infty}$. Equation (19) is to be viewed as an equation involving infinite matrices and not as holding in some Banach space (see [5]).

It is easy to see that no finite submatrix of $\lambda\mathcal{A} + \mu\mathcal{B}$ centered on the principal diagonal is invertible for any λ, μ if $\hat{A}$ is singular.

<u>Proposition 5.7.2</u> $\mathcal{A}$ has a left inverse, $\mathcal{A}^{o}$. In fact $\mathcal{A}^{o}$ may be taken as

$$\mathcal{A}^{o} = \left[\begin{array}{c|c|c|c|c|c|c} \hat{A}^{D} & \hat{B}^{D}(I-\hat{A}^{D}\hat{A}) & -\hat{B}^{D^2}\hat{A}(I-\hat{A}^{D}\hat{A}) & \hat{B}^{D^3}\hat{A}^{2}(I-\hat{A}^{D}\hat{A}) & \cdots & 0 & \cdots \\ -\hat{A}^{D^2}\hat{B} & \hat{A}^{D} & \hat{B}^{D}(I-\hat{A}^{D}\hat{A}) & -\hat{B}^{D^2}\hat{A}^{2}(I-\hat{A}^{D}\hat{A}) & \cdots & \cdot\cdot & 0 \\ \hat{A}^{D^3}\hat{B}^{2} & -\hat{A}^{D^2}\hat{B} & \hat{A}^{D} & \cdot\;\cdot\;\cdot\;\cdot\;\cdot & \cdots & \cdot & \cdot \\ \cdot & \cdot & \cdot & \cdot & \cdot\cdot & \cdot & \cdot\cdot \end{array}\right]. \tag{21}$$

Note that $\mathcal{A}^{o}$ is row finite since the $i^{\underline{th}}$ row has $k + i + 1$ nonzero entries, $k = \mathrm{Ind}(\hat{A})$. Thus

$$\mathcal{A}^{o}\mathcal{B} = S\{\hat{B}^{D^{\ell+1}}\hat{A}^{\ell-i}[I;\hat{A}]\hat{C}\}. \tag{22}$$

If $\underline{Y}(\tau)$ satisfies (19), then it satisfies $\dot{\underline{Y}}(\tau) - \mathcal{A}^{o}\mathcal{B}\underline{Y}(\tau) = \underline{0}$. Thus, formally

$$\underline{Y}(\tau) = \exp(\mathcal{A}^{o}\mathcal{B}\tau)\underline{Y}(0). \tag{23}$$

Note that (23) does define a formal power series since (22) is row finite (each row has a finite number of nonzero entries). In fact, (23) converges element wise.

Now from our earlier discussion we know that there is a solution to (19) and $\underline{Y}(0)$ is given by (12). It is not hard to see that since it exists, the solution $\underline{Y}(\tau)$ must be given by (23).

Define for the sequence $\{\alpha_i\}$, the following sequences.

$$\Sigma_{n1}(\alpha) = \alpha_n,$$

$$\Sigma_{n2}(\alpha) = \sum_{i+j=n} \alpha_i\alpha_j,$$

$$\Sigma_{n3}(\alpha) = \sum_{i+j+k=n} \alpha_i\alpha_j\alpha_k \quad , \quad \text{etc.}$$

Note that $S(\alpha) = S\{\Sigma_{11}(\alpha), \Sigma_{21}(\alpha),\ldots\}$. Then it is a simple exercise in matrix multiplication to verify that
$(S(\alpha))^m = S\{\Sigma_{mm}(\alpha), \Sigma_{m+1,m}(\alpha), \Sigma_{m+2,m}(\alpha),\ldots\}$. Taking $A^oB = S(\alpha)$ we thus get

$$\exp(A^o Bt) = S(B(\tau)), \tag{24}$$

where $\beta_1(\tau) = \exp(\alpha_1\tau)$ and, in general,

$$\beta_r(\tau) = \sum_{k=0}^{\infty} \left(\frac{\left[\Sigma_{r+k,\ k+1}(\alpha)\right] \tau^k}{k!} \right). \tag{25}$$

Thus we have

<u>Proposition 5.7.3</u> $Y_i(\tau) = \sum_{\ell=0}^{i} \beta_{\ell+1}(\tau)Y_\ell(o)$ where $\beta_{\ell+1}$ is given by (25) and $Y_\ell(0)$ by (12).

There remains two technical details. One is the convergence of (25). However, for a fixed r, the number of terms in $\Sigma_{r+k,k+1}(\alpha)$ is less than $\binom{r+k}{k+1}$, which in turn is less than $(r + k)^r$. Also, the norm of the terms in $\Sigma_{r+k,k+1}$ grows with k as $(\max_{1<j\leq r}\|A_i\|)^{k+1}$, since each factor of each term is in $\{A_1,\ldots,A_r\}$. Thus (25) converges for all τ.

We did not discuss it when developing Proposition 3 so as not to obscure the general development, but there is one additional difficulty. The preceding calculations use, quite heavily, the associativity of matrix multiplication, which does not in general hold for denumerable matrices. However $\mathcal{A}^O$ is row-finite, and $\mathcal{A}^O(\mathcal{A}\dot{\underline{Y}})$, $(\mathcal{A}^O\mathcal{A})\dot{\underline{Y}}$, $\mathcal{A}^O(\mathcal{A}\underline{Y})$, $(\mathcal{A}^O\mathcal{A})\underline{Y}$ are all well defined so that the products are associative [39, Corollary I-9]. Similarly the row finiteness of $\mathcal{A}^O\mathcal{B}$ in (22) makes the series (23) manipulate as desired. If $\mathcal{A}^O\mathcal{B}$ were not row finite one would have to consider the possibility that $\mathcal{A}^O\mathcal{B}(\mathcal{A}^O\mathcal{B})^2 \neq (\mathcal{A}^O\mathcal{B})^2\mathcal{A}^O\mathcal{B}$.

We may summarize the proceeding as follows.

<u>Theorem 5.7.2</u> Let A, B, C be n × n matrices. Suppose that there exists a λ such that $\lambda A + C$ is invertible and a μ such that $\mu A + B$ is invertible. Let $X_\varepsilon(t) = \exp((A + \varepsilon B)^{-1}Ct)$. Suppose that $\lim_{\varepsilon\to 0^+} X_\varepsilon(t)$ exists for $t \geq 0$. Then $X_\varepsilon(t) = \sum_{m=0}^{\infty} X_m(t)\varepsilon^m + \sum_{m=0}^{\infty} Y_m(\tau)\varepsilon^m$ where $\tau = t/\varepsilon^\ell$, $\ell = 1 + \max\{m|\hat{A}^m[I;\hat{A}]\hat{B}^D\hat{C} \neq 0\}$. $X_m(0)$, $Y_m(0)$ are given by (12). The $X_m(t)$ are given by Theorem 1. The $Y_m(\tau)$ are given by Proposition 3.

<u>Nonconstant $A(\varepsilon)$, $B(\varepsilon)$</u> Now suppose that A,C are analytic in ε and consider

$$\exp(A(\varepsilon)^{-1}C(\varepsilon)t). \tag{26}$$

Assume that $A(\varepsilon)^{-1}C(\varepsilon)$ has at most a pole of order ℓ at $\varepsilon = 0$ and the limit of (26) as $\varepsilon \to 0^+$ exists for $t > 0$. Let $C(\varepsilon) = \sum_{m=0}^{\infty} C_m\varepsilon^m$, $A(\varepsilon) = \sum_{m=0}^{\infty} A_m\varepsilon^m$. Apply Proposition 1 to $G(\varepsilon) = A(\varepsilon)^{-1}C(\varepsilon)$ to get $\exp(A(\varepsilon)^{-1}C(\varepsilon)t) = \exp(G_1(\varepsilon)t)P_1(\varepsilon) + \exp(G_2(\varepsilon)t)P_2(\varepsilon)$. Let C_1 be a contour including the bounded part of $\sigma(A(\varepsilon)^{-1}C(\varepsilon)) \cup \{\lambda \mid \lambda A_0 - C_0 \text{ is not invertible}\}$. Then $P_1(\varepsilon) = \frac{1}{2\pi i}\int_{C_1} (\gamma - A(\varepsilon)^{-1}C(\varepsilon))^{-1}d\gamma = \frac{1}{2\pi i}\int_{C_1} (\gamma A(\varepsilon) - C(\varepsilon))^{-1}A(\varepsilon)d\gamma$ which is analytic at $\varepsilon = 0$ since $\gamma A_0 - C_0$ is invertible on C_1. Now one must compute the power series for $P_1(\varepsilon) = \sum_{m=0}^{\infty} Q_m\varepsilon^m$. Note that

$$Q_0 = P_1(0) = \frac{1}{2\pi i}\int_{C_1} (\gamma A_0 - C_0)^{-1}d\gamma = [(\lambda A_0 - C_0)^{-1}A_0]^D[(\lambda A_0 - C_0)^{-1}A_0].$$

Also by differentiating under the integral sign one may compute all of the other coefficients. For example, $Q_1 = -\frac{1}{2\pi i}\int_{C_1} (\gamma A_0 - C_0)^{-1}A_1(\gamma A_0 - C_0)^{-1}d\gamma$.

Thus we again have $\exp(A(\varepsilon)C(\varepsilon)^{-1}t) = \sum_{m=0}^{\infty} X_m(t)\varepsilon^m + \sum_{m=0}^{\infty} Y_m(\tau)\varepsilon^m$ and both series satisfy $A(\varepsilon)\dot{Z} = C(\varepsilon)Z$. The X_k satisfy for $k \geq 1$,

$$\begin{aligned} &A_0\dot{X}_k(t) + A_1\dot{X}_{k-1}(t) + \ldots + A_k\dot{X}_0(t) = \\ &C_oX_k(t) + C_1X_{k-1}(t) + \ldots + C_kX_0(t). \end{aligned} \tag{27}$$

Since the $X_k(0)$ are computable by our earlier comments and since $\lambda A_0 - C_0$ is assumed invertible, (27) uniquely determines X_k in terms of $X_{k-1},\ldots,X_0$. Note that X_0 is still given by (15) except A_0, C_0 replace A, C and the $X_{m-1}(t)$ in (16) is replaced by $-A_1\dot{X}_{k-1}(t) - \ldots -A_k\dot{X}_0(t) + C_1X_{k-1}(t) + \ldots + C_kX_0(t)$. To handle the $Y_k(\tau)$ we insert the series $\sum_{m=0}^{\infty} Y_m(\tau)\varepsilon^m$ into $A(\varepsilon)\frac{dy}{d\tau} = \varepsilon^\ell C(\varepsilon)Y$ to give

$$A_o\dot{Y}_o(\tau) = 0$$

$$\vdots$$

$$A_o\dot{Y}_{\ell-1}(\tau) + A_1\dot{Y}_{\ell-2}(\tau) + \ldots + A_{\ell-1}\dot{Y}_o(\tau) = 0 \tag{28}$$

$$\sum_{m=0}^{\ell+j} A_m\dot{Y}_{\ell+j-m}(\tau) = \sum_{i=0}^{j} C_iY_{\ell-i} \quad , \quad j \geq 0.$$

Rewriting (28) gives $A\dot{\underline{Y}} - C\underline{Y} = \underline{0}$ where $A = S\{A_{i-1}\}$, $C = S\{0,\ldots,0,C_o,C_1,\ldots\}$. As before A is not invertible.

At this point we encounter some problems which we have not been able to completely surmount. If A has a left inverse which is row finite, or some other appropriate property, then the rest of the solution proceeds as before. However we do not know if, in general, A has a left inverse. Such a determination would depend on the particular relationships between the A_i's. We do point out that it is relatively easy to show that A is probably one to one since A is one to one on the set of sequences which grow as the $i^{\underline{th}}$ power of some number. The important thing to determine is a row finite left inverse. In general, it is possible to have an invertible matrix with a zero eigenvalue [39].

The asymptotic expansion of (2) is also treated in [45] under the same type of assumptions we make. However [45] does not discuss sufficient conditions. Whereas we find the appropriate initial conditions and actually solve the infinite systems of equations for the coefficients, [45], in essence, gives an infinite system and says this is it. [45] also makes no use of the functional calculus as we do which makes determination of the initial values and the coefficients much easier.

8. SOME APPLICATIONS

The manner in which singularly perturbed systems arise was discussed in Chapter 2. This section will show how the results of Sections 3, 4, 5 can be applied to particular systems. Consider

$$\begin{aligned} \dot{\underline{x}} &= A_1(\varepsilon)\underline{x} + A_2(\varepsilon)\underline{y} \\ \varepsilon\dot{\underline{y}} &= B_1(\varepsilon)\underline{x} + B_2(\varepsilon)\underline{y} \end{aligned} \tag{1}$$

with the initial conditions $\underline{x}(0) = \underline{x}_o$, $\underline{y}(0) = \underline{y}_o$ and the corresponding reduced system,

$$\begin{aligned} \dot{\underline{x}} &= A_1\underline{x} + A_2\underline{y} \\ \underline{0} &= B_1\underline{x} + B_2\underline{y} \end{aligned} \tag{2}$$

where $A_i(\varepsilon) \to A_i$, $B_i(\varepsilon) \to B_i$ for $i = 1,2$ as $\varepsilon \to 0^+$ and $B_1(\varepsilon)$, $B_2(\varepsilon)$ are right differentiable at $\varepsilon = 0$.

Theorem 5.8.1 The solution $(\underline{x}_\varepsilon(t), \underline{y}_\varepsilon(t))$ of (1) has a pointwise limit for $t > 0$ for all $(\underline{x}_o, \underline{y}_o)$ if and only if $B = \begin{bmatrix} 0 & 0 \\ B_1 & B_2 \end{bmatrix}$ is semistable. B is semistable if and only if B_2 is semistable and $B_2^D B_2 B_1 = B_1$. If B is semistable, then $(\underline{x}_\varepsilon(t), \underline{y}_\varepsilon(t))$ converges to a solution of the reduced problem. Let $(\underline{x}(t), \underline{y}(t))$ be this limiting solution. Then

$$\begin{bmatrix} \underline{x}(t) \\ \underline{y}(t) \end{bmatrix} = e^{[\hat{A}(0),B]t}[I;B]\begin{bmatrix} \underline{x}_o \\ \underline{y}_o \end{bmatrix} \tag{3}$$

where $\hat{A}(\varepsilon) = \begin{bmatrix} A_1(\varepsilon) & A_2(\varepsilon) \\ \dot{B}_1(0) & \dot{B}_2(0) \end{bmatrix}$. If the $B_i(\varepsilon)$ are constant, then (3) is

$$\begin{bmatrix} \underline{x}(t) \\ \underline{y}(t) \end{bmatrix} = \begin{bmatrix} e^{(A_1-A_2B_2{}^DB_1)t}\underline{x}(0) + \Theta((A_1-A_2B_2{}^DB_1)t)A_2[I;B_2]t\underline{y}(0) \\ -B_2{}^DB_1\underline{x}(t) + [I;B_2]\underline{y}(0) \end{bmatrix} \tag{4}$$

where $\Theta(z) = (e^z - 1)/z$. All limiting solutions satisfy the initial conditions

$$B^D B \begin{bmatrix} \underline{x}(0) \\ \underline{y}(0) \end{bmatrix} = \begin{bmatrix} \underline{0} \\ \underline{0} \end{bmatrix}.$$

<u>Proof</u> Let $A(\varepsilon) = \begin{bmatrix} A_1(\varepsilon) & A_2(\varepsilon) \\ 0 & 0 \end{bmatrix}$, $B(\varepsilon) = \begin{bmatrix} 0 & 0 \\ B_1(\varepsilon) & B_2(\varepsilon) \end{bmatrix}$. Then all solutions of (1) are of the form: $\underline{z}_\varepsilon(t) = \begin{bmatrix} \underline{x}_\varepsilon(t) \\ \underline{y}_\varepsilon(t) \end{bmatrix} = e^{(A(\varepsilon) + B(\varepsilon)/\varepsilon)t} \begin{bmatrix} \underline{x}(0) \\ \underline{y}(0) \end{bmatrix}$. By Theorem 4.1, $\underline{z}_\varepsilon(t)$ has a limit for all $\underline{x}_o, \underline{y}_o$ if and only if B is semistable. But $\sigma(B) = \sigma(B_2) \cup \{0\}$, and $\begin{bmatrix} 0 & 0 \\ B_1 & B_2 \end{bmatrix}^D = \begin{bmatrix} 0 & 0 \\ (B_2^D)^2 B_1 & B_2^D \end{bmatrix}$. Thus one can easily verify that B has index 1 if and only if B_2 has index 0 or 1 and $B_2^D B_2 B_1 = B_1$. (3) follows from Theorem 4.1. Suppose then Ind(B) = 1 and the $B_i(\varepsilon)$ are constant. Let $\Phi(t) = \Theta((A_1 - A_2 B_2^D B_1)t)$ where $\Theta(z)$ has the power series expansion $(e^z - 1)/z$. Then

$$[I;B]e^{[A;B]t} = \left[\begin{array}{c|c} e^{(A_1 - A_2 B_2^D B_1)t} & \Phi(t) A_2 [I;B_2] t \\ \hline -B_2^D B_1 e^{(A_1 - A_2 B_2^D B_1)t} & -B_2^D B_1 \Phi(t) A_2 [I;B_2] t + [I;B_2] \end{array}\right]. \quad (5)$$

Theorem 4.1 shows that to describe the limits of $\underline{x}_\varepsilon, \underline{y}_\varepsilon$, we may assume $\begin{bmatrix} \underline{x}_o \\ \underline{y}_o \end{bmatrix} \in \mathcal{R}([I;B])$. Then $B_2^D B_2 \underline{y}_o = -B_2^D B_1 \underline{x}_o$, $\underline{x}_o$ arbitrary and (4) follows from (5). That (4) is a solution of (2) follows from the uniform convergence of $\underline{x}_\varepsilon(t)$, $\dot{\underline{x}}_\varepsilon(t)$, $\underline{y}_\varepsilon(t)$, $\dot{\underline{y}}_\varepsilon(t)$ on compact subsets of $(0,\infty)$. □

Note that if B is semistable, then the solution of (1) can be written

$$\begin{bmatrix} \underline{x}_\varepsilon(t) \\ \underline{y}_\varepsilon(t) \end{bmatrix} = e^{[\hat{A}(o),B]t}[I;B] \begin{bmatrix} \underline{x}_o \\ \underline{y}_o \end{bmatrix} + e^{(A(\varepsilon) + B(\varepsilon)/\varepsilon)t} BB^D \begin{bmatrix} \underline{x}_o \\ \underline{y}_o \end{bmatrix} + E(t) \begin{bmatrix} \underline{x}_o \\ \underline{y}_o \end{bmatrix}$$

where the first term is the solution of the reduced problem (2), the second term is the "boundary layer correction" and $E(t) \to 0$ uniformly on $[0,t_o]$ for every $t > 0$ as $\varepsilon \to 0^+$.

Nonhomogeneous equations

In considering a nonhomogeneous version of (1), we shall use control theory terminology. (See Section 2.2.)

Consider the following system,

$$\begin{cases} \dot{\underline{x}} = A_1(\varepsilon)\underline{x} + A_2(\varepsilon)\underline{y} + A_3(\varepsilon)\underline{u} \\ \varepsilon\dot{\underline{y}} = B_1(\varepsilon)\underline{x} + B_2(\varepsilon)\underline{y} + B_3(\varepsilon)\underline{u} \end{cases} \tag{6}$$

where ε is a small parameter. Here $\underline{x} \in \mathbb{C}^n$, $\underline{y} \in \mathbb{C}^m$, $\underline{u} \in \mathbb{C}^r$. The $A_i(\varepsilon)$, $B_i(\varepsilon)$, $C_i(\varepsilon)$ are analytic functions of ε and $X_i^o(0) = X_i$ for $X = A,B,C$. The $\underline{x}$, $\underline{y}$ represent the state of the plant and $\underline{u}$ is the control. All matrices, and in particular, $B_2(0)$, are allowed to be singular.

The reduced system associated with (6) is

$$\begin{cases} \dot{\underline{x}} = A_1^o\underline{x} + A_2^o\underline{y} + A_3^o\underline{u} \\ \underline{0} = B_1^o\underline{x} + B_2^o\underline{y} + B_3^o\underline{u} \end{cases} \tag{7}$$

We shall examine the limit of solutions of (6). In all cases in which we establish the existence of limits, they will satisfy (7) for $t > 0$ though the initial conditions will no longer necessarily be satisfied. The process (6), of course, is basic to a variety of control problems such as time-optimal and quadratic-regulator.

Solution of (6)

Let $A(\varepsilon) = \begin{bmatrix} A_1(\varepsilon) & A_2(\varepsilon) \\ 0 & 0 \end{bmatrix}$, $B(\varepsilon) = \begin{bmatrix} 0 & 0 \\ B_1(\varepsilon) & B_2(\varepsilon) \end{bmatrix}$, $\underline{z} = \begin{bmatrix} \underline{x} \\ \underline{y} \end{bmatrix}$ and $C(\varepsilon) = \begin{bmatrix} A_3(\varepsilon) \\ B_3(\varepsilon) \end{bmatrix}$. Then (1) may be written as

$$\dot{\underline{z}}_3 = (A(\varepsilon) + B(\varepsilon)/\varepsilon)\underline{z} + \varepsilon^{-1}C(\varepsilon)\underline{u} \tag{8}$$

An elementary calculation gives that

$$\underline{z}_\varepsilon(t) = \int_0^t \exp((A(\varepsilon) + B(\varepsilon)/\varepsilon)(t - s))\varepsilon^{-1}C(\varepsilon)\underline{u}(s)ds + \exp((A(\varepsilon) + B(\varepsilon)/\varepsilon)t)\underline{z}(0). \tag{9}$$

We wish to determine when (9) has a limit as $\varepsilon \to 0^+$ and what the limit is when it exists. Note that both Theorem 2 and Theorem 3 provide necessary and sufficient conditions.

Theorem 5.8.2 $\underline{z}_\varepsilon(t)$ has a limit as $\varepsilon \to 0^+$ for every $\underline{z}(0)$ for some control $\underline{u}(t)$ if and only if $B(0)$ is semistable.

Proof Suppose $\underline{z}_\varepsilon(t)$ has a limit as $\varepsilon \to 0^+$ for every $\underline{z}(0)$ for some $\underline{u}(t)$. Taking the difference of (9) for two different $\underline{z}(0)$ we get $\exp((A(\varepsilon) + B(\varepsilon)/\varepsilon)t)(\underline{z}_1(0) - \underline{z}_2(0))$ has a limit as $\varepsilon \to 0^+$ for every $\underline{z}_1(0)$, $\underline{z}_2(0)$. Hence $\exp((A(\varepsilon) + B(\varepsilon)/\varepsilon)t)$ has a limit as $\varepsilon \to 0^+$. But by Theorem 4.1 this happens if and only if $B(0)$ is semistable. Conversely, if $B(0)$ is semistable, then $\underline{z}_\varepsilon(t)$ has a limit for $\underline{u}(t) \equiv \underline{0}$. $\square$

Suppose then $B(0)$ is semistable. We wish to determine for which $\underline{u}(t)$ (9) has a limit as $\varepsilon \to 0$. Since $B(0)$ is semistable, it suffices to determine for what $\underline{u}(t)$ the integral has a limit as $\varepsilon \to 0^+$. Define $P_0(\varepsilon)$, $P_1(\varepsilon)$ as in the proof of Theorem 4.1 so that $\exp((A(\varepsilon) + B(\varepsilon)/\varepsilon)t) = \exp(F_0(\varepsilon)t)P_0(\varepsilon) +$

$\exp(F_1(\varepsilon)t)P_1(\varepsilon)$. $\underline{z}_\varepsilon(t)$ has a limit as $\varepsilon \to 0^+$ if and only if $P_i(\varepsilon)\underline{z}_\varepsilon(t)$ has a limit for i = 0, 1. But $\|P_1(\varepsilon)\underline{z}_\varepsilon(t)\| = O(e^{\mu t/\varepsilon})$ where μ is any number such that $\mu < 0$ and $\mu > \mathrm{Re}\lambda$ for all $\lambda \in \sigma(B(0))$ such that $\mathrm{Re}\lambda < 0$. Thus to determine the existence of limiting behavior of (9) it suffices to consider $P_0(\varepsilon)\underline{z}_\varepsilon(t)$. Now

$$
\begin{aligned}
&P_1(\varepsilon) \int_0^t \exp((A(\varepsilon) + B(\varepsilon)/\varepsilon)(t - s)) \frac{1}{\varepsilon} C(\varepsilon)\underline{u}(s)ds \\
&= \int_0^t \exp((A(\varepsilon) + B(\varepsilon)/\varepsilon)(t - s)P_1(\varepsilon) \frac{1}{\varepsilon} C(\varepsilon)\underline{u}(s)ds.
\end{aligned}
\tag{10}
$$

Since B(0) is semistable, $\exp((A(\varepsilon) + B(\varepsilon)/\varepsilon)(t - s))P_1(\varepsilon) = \sum_{k=0}^{\infty} X_n(t - s)\varepsilon^n$ where the X_n are given in Section 4. Let $C(\varepsilon) = \sum_{k=0}^{\infty} C_k\varepsilon^k$. Then (10) becomes

$$
\frac{1}{\varepsilon}\int_0^t X_0(t - s)C_0\underline{u}(s)ds + \sum_{k=0}^{\infty}\left[\sum_{\ell=0}^{k+1}\int_0^t X_{k+1-\ell}(t - s)C_\ell\underline{u}(s)ds\right]\varepsilon^k. \tag{11}
$$

(11) provides an explicit expansion of $P_1(\varepsilon)\underline{z}_\varepsilon(t)$. Now (11) will have a limit, obviously, if and only if

$$
\int_0^t X_0(t - s)C_0\underline{u}(s)ds \equiv \underline{0}. \tag{12}
$$

But $X_0(t) = \exp([A(o) + \dot{B}(0)\ ;B(0)]t)[I;B(0)]$ from Theorem 4.1. Thus if B(0) is semistable, then (9) will have a limit as $\varepsilon \to 0^+$ if and only if

$$
\int_0^t \exp([A(0) + \dot{B}(0)])[I;B(0)]C_0\underline{u}(s)ds \equiv \underline{0}. \tag{13}
$$

Theorem 5.8.3 If B(0) is semistable, then (10) will have a limit as $\varepsilon \to 0^+$ if and only if

$$
[I;B(0)]C_0\underline{u}(t) \equiv \underline{0}. \tag{14}
$$

The limit, when it exists, is given for all $t > 0$ by

$$\int_0^t \{X_1(t-s)C_0 + X_0(t-s)C_1\}\underline{u}(s)ds$$
$$+ \exp([A(0) + \dot{B}(0)\ ;B(0)]t)[I;B(0)]\underline{z}(0) \tag{15}$$

Proof The first part of Theorem 3 follows from (13) by differentiating with respect to t and then multiplying by $\exp([A(0) + \dot{B}(0)\ ;B(0)]t)$. Since $P_2(\varepsilon)\underline{z}_\varepsilon(t) \to \underline{0}$ for $t > 0$, as $\varepsilon \to 0^+$, we need only compute $P_1(0)\underline{z}_0(t)$. By (11) and (13), this is $\int_0^t X_1(t-s)C_0\underline{u}(s) + X_0(t-s)C_1\underline{u}(s)ds +$ $\exp([A(0) + \dot{B}(0)\ ;B(0)]t)[I;B(0)]\underline{z}(0)$ as desired. □

Note that the limit satisfies (7) and the initial condition $[I;B(0)]\underline{z}(0)$ and not $\underline{z}(0)$. It is also worth noting that we actually have the full expansion of the inner solution of $\underline{z}_\varepsilon(t)$. The outer solution is also easily gotten. From Section 4,

$$P_2(\varepsilon)\exp((A(\varepsilon) + B(\varepsilon)/\varepsilon)t) = \sum_{k=0}^{\infty} Y_k(\tau)\varepsilon^k \text{ where } \tau = t/\varepsilon. \tag{16}$$

Thus if $\rho = s/\varepsilon$,

$$P_2(\varepsilon)\underline{z}_\varepsilon(t) = \int_0^\tau \sum_{k=0}^{\infty} (\tau - \rho)\varepsilon^k C(\varepsilon)\underline{u}(\varepsilon\rho)d\rho + \sum_{k=0}^{\infty} Y_k(\tau)\varepsilon^k \underline{z}(0).$$

The $Y_k(\tau)$ are given explicitly in Sections 3, 4. Depending on the smoothness of $\underline{u}$ one may get the necessary initial terms. In particular, for fixed τ,

$$\lim_{\varepsilon\to 0^+} P_2(\varepsilon)\underline{z}_\varepsilon(\varepsilon\tau) = \int_0^\tau Y_0(\tau-\rho)C(0)\underline{u}(0)d\rho + Y_0(\tau)\underline{z}(0).$$

If $\underline{u}$ is analytic, and $\underline{u}(t) = \sum_{i=0}^{\infty} \underline{u}_i t^i$, then

$$P_2(\varepsilon)\underline{z}_\varepsilon(t) = \sum_{k=0}^{\infty} \left\{ \sum_{i+j+r=k} \int_0^\tau Y_i(\tau - \rho)C_j\underline{u}_r\rho^r d\rho + Y_k(\tau)\underline{z}(0) \right\} \varepsilon^k. \quad (17)$$

Note that the reduced problem (7) is not consistent for all controls. Condition (14) is equivalent to saying that $\underline{u}(t)$ is an admissable control for the reduced problem.

One could also consider systems with small parameters of different orders, such as

$$\begin{aligned} \dot{\underline{x}} &= A_1(\varepsilon)\underline{x} + A_2(\varepsilon)\underline{y} + A_3(\varepsilon)\underline{z} + A_4(\varepsilon)\underline{u} \\ \varepsilon\dot{\underline{y}} &= B_1(\varepsilon)\underline{x} + B_2(\varepsilon)\underline{y} + B_3(\varepsilon)\underline{z} + B_4(\varepsilon)\underline{u} \\ \varepsilon^2\dot{\underline{z}} &= C_1(\varepsilon)\underline{x} + C_2(\varepsilon)\underline{y} + C_3(\varepsilon)\underline{z} + C_4(\varepsilon)\underline{u}. \end{aligned} \quad (18)$$

For (18), one would use Section 5.

As another possibility, it may be that certain linear combinations of derivatives may be multiplied by small parameters, so that one would consider a singularly perturbed process of the form

$$(A + \varepsilon B)\dot{\underline{x}} = C(\varepsilon)\underline{x} + D(\varepsilon)\underline{u} \quad (19)$$

or, more generally,

$$A(\varepsilon)\dot{\underline{x}} = C(\varepsilon)\underline{x} + D(\varepsilon)\underline{u}. \quad (20)$$

The process (19) has also been studied in [45]. However, [45] does not determine sufficient conditions and explicitly compute the expansions as we do. No use of contour integrals is made in [45].

If one starts by assuming $B(0)$ is semistable and $[I;B(0)]C_o\underline{u}(t) \equiv \underline{0}$, then by performing the appropriate similarities, it is possible to get the limit of (9) existing without all our machinery. But this only provides the sufficiency of the conditions discussed. To get the necessity parts of Theorems 2 and 3 requires our earlier work.

While most authors when studying (6) assume $B_2(0)$ is invertible, [41], [60], the singular case has been studied by several authors, for example, [58], [36]. Both [42] and [58] assume some type of semistability. Our work differs in two respects from most previous work. Unlike [36], [58] we derive necessary as well as sufficient conditions (admittedly in a simpler setting). We also do not make the usual controllability assumptions. Neither need we make the nonsingularity assumptions on B^TQB of [56] or the full rank condition on C_oB_o in [68]. Secondly, in [4] and [62] the entire derivative in (6) is multiplied by ε so that the reduced problem is not a differential equation, but rather a functional equation. Finally, we should point out our approach does not involve matching. By using contour integrals, the exponential is broken into two terms and these terms are computed separately. Our series actually converge to the indicated terms.

9. PRODUCTS OF EXPONENTIALS

The results and techniques of the preceding sections can also be used to analyze certain products of exponentials. Since these results are not directly related to the main topic of this book we shall omit their proof. The interested reader is referred to [7]. These results generalize a result from [25], which played a basic role in Ellis and Pinsky's analysis of the Navier-Stokes equations [25], [26].

Kato in [37] generalized the results of [25] to a Hilbert space.

In this section we shall show how the results of the preceding sections can be used to determine precisely when

$$\lim_{\varepsilon\to 0^+} \exp[(A + B/\varepsilon)t]\exp[-tB/\varepsilon] \tag{1}$$

exists for $n \times n$ matrices A,B. In particular, we shall completely characterize those B for which (1) exists for all A. The extension to operators will then be briefly discussed. A matrix will be called simple if it is similar to a diagonal matrix.

The basic result from which our other results follow is,

Theorem 5.9.1 Suppose that A,B are $n \times n$ matrices and B is simple. Let $\{\lambda_1,\ldots,\lambda_r\} = \sigma(B)$ be the eigenvalues of B. Define $P_{\lambda_j} = \frac{1}{2\pi i}\int_{C_j} (\lambda - B)^{-1} d\lambda$ where C_j is a contour with λ_j in its interior and λ_k for $k \neq j$ in its exterior. Then $\exp[(A + B/\varepsilon)t]\exp[-tB/\varepsilon]$ has a limit as $\varepsilon \to 0^+$ for all $t \geq 0$ if and only if $P_{\lambda_j} A P_{\lambda_k} = 0$ for $\mathrm{Re}(\lambda_j - \lambda_k) > 0$. The limit, when it exists, is

$$\exp(tA_o),\ A_o = \sum_{\lambda\in\sigma(B)} P_\lambda A P_\lambda. \tag{2}$$

As an immediate consequence of Theorem 1, we have

Theorem 5.9.2 Suppose that A,B are $n \times n$ matrices and B is simple. Then $\exp[t(A + B/\varepsilon)]\exp[-tB/\varepsilon]$ has a limit as $\varepsilon \to 0^+$ for all t if and only if $P_{\lambda_j} A P_{\lambda_k} = 0$ for λ_j,λ_k such that $\mathrm{Re}(\lambda_j - \lambda_k) \neq 0$. The limit when it exists is given by (2).

In a certain sense, the converse of Theorem 2 holds,

Theorem 5.9.3 Suppose that B is an $n \times n$ matrix. Then $\exp[t(A + B/\varepsilon)]\exp[-tB/\varepsilon]$ exists for all $n \times n$ matrices A for all t as $\varepsilon \to 0^+$ if and only if B is simple and all eigenvalues of B have the same real part. The limit, when it exists, if given by (2).

Theorem 1 is of some independent interest, as the next example illustrates.

Example 5.9.1

$$\lim_{\varepsilon\to 0^+} \exp\left(\begin{bmatrix} -1/\varepsilon & 1 \\ 0 & 0 \end{bmatrix} t\right) \exp\left(\begin{bmatrix} 1/\varepsilon & 0 \\ 0 & 0 \end{bmatrix} t\right) = I \tag{3}$$

whereas

$$\lim_{\varepsilon\to 0^+} \exp\left(\begin{bmatrix} 1/\varepsilon & 1 \\ 0 & 0 \end{bmatrix} t\right) \exp\left(\begin{bmatrix} -1/\varepsilon & 0 \\ 0 & 0 \end{bmatrix} t\right) \tag{4}$$

fails to exist. To see (3) note that $P_{-1} = \begin{bmatrix} 1 & 0 \\ 0 & 0 \end{bmatrix}$, $P_o = \begin{bmatrix} 0 & 0 \\ 0 & 1 \end{bmatrix}$, and $A = \begin{bmatrix} 0 & 1 \\ 0 & 0 \end{bmatrix}$. Since $P_oAP_{-1} = 0$, $P_oAP_o = 0$, $P_{-1}AP_{-1} = 0$, we have (3) by Theorem 1. On the other hand, in (4) again $A = \begin{bmatrix} 0 & 1 \\ 0 & 0 \end{bmatrix}$, but $P_1 = \begin{bmatrix} 1 & 0 \\ 0 & 0 \end{bmatrix}$, $P_o = \begin{bmatrix} 0 & 0 \\ 0 & 1 \end{bmatrix}$ and $P_1AP_o \neq 0$ so that the limit will fail to exist.

If B is a bounded operator which is similar to a diagonal matrix and the eigenvalues of B can be isolated by contours, then Theorem 1 and 2 can be easily carried through. Theorem 3 uses the finite dimensionality of the eigenspace. One could, however, extend Theorem 3 to compact operators B such that the closed linear span of the generalized eigenspaces for nonzero eigenvalues was the whole space and A was an arbitrary bounded linear operator. Note that this extension differs from Kato's in that he assumed A compact and B self-adjoint.

6 Nonautonomous systems

1. INTRODUCTION

This chapter shall be concerned with the differential equation

$$A\dot{\underline{x}} + B\underline{x} = \underline{f} \tag{1}$$

and the associated homogeneous equation

$$A\dot{\underline{x}} + B\underline{x} = \underline{0} \tag{2}$$

where $\underline{x}$ is a $\mathbb{C}^n$ valued function of a real variable t, and A,B are $\mathbb{C}^{n\times n}$ valued functions, differentiable in t. A,B are both allowed to be singular. There are essentially two distinct classes of problems involved here.

Type I. Describe solutions and consistent initial conditions for an interval (t_1,t_2) on which the appropriate "structure" of the system, for example the rank, index, or core-rank of some appropriate matrix, is constant.

Type II. Describe solutions around a point t_o where the structure is different from the structure on a deleted neighborhood of t_o.

In the case when A(t) is invertible for $0 < |t-t_o| < \delta$, and $A(t_o)$ is singular, we have a Type II problem that has been widely studied. See, for example, [28], [64]. In this case, the description of the solutions involves series type techniques.

In Chapter 3, (1) was solved with A,B constant and $\lambda A + B$ invertible for some scalar λ. The solution involves a blend of reductions to canonical forms, and solutions of a nonsingular problem. This is an example of what we are calling a Type I problem.

Type I problems in general have not been as well studied as some of the Type II problems have. Type I problems are also more in keeping with the spirit of this book and are the type we shall concentrate on. Of course, the complete solution of (1) will eventually require the combining of the information on both types of problems.

The definition of a Type I problem is intentionally vague. One of our purposes is to investigate when (1) is a pure Type I problem. That is, can be solved without having to deal with the "turning point behavior" that occurs in Type II problems.

We shall first investigate when (1) can be reduced to a constant coefficient equation. We then consider the general nonautonomous problem. Finally, we shall consider nonautonomous discrete equations. Since, in general, useful explicit solutions to (1) are lacking even when A is invertible, we should not expect to obtain such explicit solutions when A is singular.

At this time a complete solution of the Type I problem is not available. We shall present some of the basic theory and give two techniques that will solve a large number of the more frequently encountered systems.

2. REDUCTION TO CONSTANT COEFFICIENTS

Since (1.1) is much easier to solve if A,B are constants, it could be helpful to know when (1.1) can be made to have constant coefficients by a change of variables $\underline{x} = L\underline{y}$, L(t) invertible.

Theorem 6.2.1 Let A(t),B(t),$\underline{f}$(t) be continuously differentiable functions defined on an interval I. Then $A\dot{\underline{x}} + B\underline{x} = \underline{f}$ can be transformed to

$$E\dot{\underline{y}} + F\underline{y} = \underline{f}; \qquad E,F \text{ constant} \quad \lambda E + F \text{ invertible}, \tag{1}$$

for $t \in I$ by an invertible transformation $\underline{x} = L\underline{y}$ if and only if

(i) There exists a scalar λ such that $B + \lambda A - \dot{A}$ is invertible on I, and

(ii) $A(B + \lambda A - \dot{A})^{-1}$ is constant on I.

If (i) and (ii) hold, one may take $L = (B + \lambda A - \dot{A})^{-1}$, $C = A(A + \lambda A - \dot{A})^{-1}$ and the transformed equation is

$$C\dot{\underline{y}} + (I - \lambda C)\underline{y} = \underline{f}. \tag{2}$$

Proof Let $\underline{x} = L\underline{y}$. Then $A\dot{\underline{x}} + B\underline{x} = \underline{f}$ becomes $(AL)\dot{\underline{y}} + (A\dot{L} + BL)\underline{y} = \underline{f}$. Suppose $AL = E$, $(A\dot{L} + BL) = F$ are constants. Then $A\dot{L} + \dot{L}A = 0$ so that $AL = E$, $(B - \dot{A})L = F$. If there is a λ such that $\lambda E + F$ is invertible, then $(\lambda A + B - \dot{A})L = \lambda E + F$ so that (i) holds. But $L = (\lambda A + B - \dot{A})^{-1}(\lambda E + F)$ and $AL = E$ so that (ii) holds. Conversely suppose that (i), (ii) hold. Let $L = (B + \lambda A - \dot{A})^{-1}$ and $C = A(B + \lambda A - \dot{A})^{-1}$. Then $AL = C$ and $\lambda AL + (B - \dot{A})L = I$ so that $(B - \dot{A})L = I - \lambda C$ and (2) follows. □

Note that if (ii) holds, then $\mathcal{R}(A)$ is constant.

Theorem 1 is strictly a singular result since if A is invertible, letting L^{-1} be the fundamental matrix solution of $\dot{\underline{x}} + A^{-1}B\underline{x} = \underline{0}$ will always give $\dot{\underline{y}} = \underline{0}$. The idea of using $\underline{x} = L\underline{y}$ to transform to constant coefficients also appears in stability theory, but additional restraints are put on L. See [28].

Example 6.2.1 Let $A(t) = \begin{bmatrix} 1 & t \\ 0 & 0 \end{bmatrix}$, $B(t) = \begin{bmatrix} 0 & 0 \\ 1 & t \end{bmatrix}$. Note that $\lambda A + B$ is singular for all λ, t. For $\lambda = 0$, $B + \lambda A - \dot{A} = \begin{bmatrix} 0 & -1 \\ 1 & t \end{bmatrix}$ is nonsingular for all t. Let $L = \begin{bmatrix} 0 & -1 \\ 1 & t \end{bmatrix}^{-1} = \begin{bmatrix} t & 1 \\ -1 & 0 \end{bmatrix}$. Note that $AL = \begin{bmatrix} 0 & 1 \\ 0 & 0 \end{bmatrix}$. Hence

$A\dot{\underline{x}} + B\underline{x} = \underline{f}$ becomes $\begin{bmatrix} 0 & 1 \\ 0 & 0 \end{bmatrix} \dot{\underline{y}} + \begin{bmatrix} 1 & 0 \\ 0 & 1 \end{bmatrix} \underline{y} = \underline{f}$; or, $C\dot{\underline{y}} + \underline{y} = \underline{f}$. By Theorem 3.1.3, the solution is $\underline{y} = \underline{f} + C\dot{\underline{f}}$. Thus $\underline{x}(t) = \begin{bmatrix} t & 1 \\ -1 & 0 \end{bmatrix} \begin{bmatrix} f_1 - \dot{f}_2 \\ f_2 \end{bmatrix}$ $= \begin{bmatrix} tf_1 - t\dot{f}_2 + f_2 \\ -f_1 - \dot{f}_2 \end{bmatrix}$. Note that in this example, $A\dot{\underline{x}} + B\underline{x} = \underline{0}$ has only the trivial solution.

Corollary 6.2.1 If conditions (i), (ii) of Theorem 1 are met, then solutions to (1) are uniquely determined by their initial value at any $t_o \in I$. Furthermore the set of consistent initial conditions at t_o is just $L(t_o)M$ where M is the flat of initial conditions for (2) given in Theorem 3.1.3.

At first glance Theorem 1 seems of limited value since finding a λ that satisfies condition (ii) would seem difficult. The next result shows that, in fact, one need only check one λ for which $B + \lambda A - \dot{A}$ is invertible.

Theorem 6.2.2 Suppose that there exists a λ such that (i) and (ii) of Theorem 1 hold. Then $A(\mu A + B - \dot{A})^{-1} = C_\mu$ is independent of t for all μ for which $\mu A + B - \dot{A}$ is invertible. Furthermore $C_\mu^D C_\mu$, $C_\mu^D(I - \mu C_\mu)$ are independent of μ.

Proof Suppose λ satisfies (i) and (ii). Clearly $C_\mu = A(\mu A + B - \dot{A})^{-1}$ is analytic in μ for all μ such that $\mu A + B - \dot{A}$ is invertible. Thus it suffices to verify Theorem 2 for μ such that $\mu A + B - \dot{A}$ is invertible and $I + (\mu - \lambda)C_\lambda$ is invertible. Now $A = C_\lambda(\lambda A + B - \dot{A}) = C_\mu(\mu A + B - \dot{A})$ $= C_\mu(\lambda A + B - \dot{A}) + C_\mu(\mu - \lambda)A$. Using the second and fourth of these expressions gives $(C_\lambda - C_\mu)(\lambda A + B - \dot{A}) = C_\mu(\mu - \lambda)A$. Thus $C_\lambda - C_\mu = C_\mu(\mu - \lambda)C_\lambda$, or equivalently, $C_\mu = (I + (\mu - \lambda)C_\lambda)^{-1}C_\lambda$. Hence C_μ is independent of t if C_λ is and C_μ, C_λ, C_μ^D, C_λ^D all commute, so that

$C_\mu^D C_\mu = [(I + (\mu - \lambda)C_\lambda)^{-1}C_\lambda]^D(I + (\mu - \lambda)C_\lambda)^{-1}C_\lambda = C_\lambda^D C_\lambda$. Also

$C_\mu^D(I - \mu C_\mu) = (I + (\mu - \lambda)C_\lambda)C_\lambda^D(I - \mu C_\lambda(I + (\mu - \lambda)C_\lambda)^{-1})$

$= C_\lambda^D(I + (\mu - \lambda)C_\lambda - \mu C_\lambda) = C_\lambda^D(I - \lambda C_\lambda)$. □

While Theorem 1 does not require $\lambda A + B$ to be invertible for some λ, in many important applications A is constant. For example, in the control problem $\begin{bmatrix} I & 0 \\ 0 & 0 \end{bmatrix}\begin{bmatrix} \dot{\underline{x}} \\ \underline{y} \end{bmatrix} + \begin{bmatrix} A & B \\ D & 0 \end{bmatrix}\begin{bmatrix} \underline{x} \\ \underline{y} \end{bmatrix} = \begin{bmatrix} C\underline{u} \\ E\underline{u} \end{bmatrix}$, $\begin{bmatrix} I & 0 \\ 0 & 0 \end{bmatrix}$ is constant.

<u>Corollary 6.2.2</u> If A in (1) is constant, then (1) can be transformed to (2) by $\underline{x} = L\underline{y}$ if and only if $\lambda A + B$ is invertible on I for some λ and $A(\lambda A + B)^{-1}$ is constant.

<u>Example 6.2.2</u> Let $A = \begin{bmatrix} 1 & t \\ t & t^2 \end{bmatrix}$, $B = \begin{bmatrix} 0 & 1 \\ 1 & 2t \end{bmatrix}$. Clearly $\lambda A + B$ is invertible for some λ. But $\lambda A + B - \dot{A} = \lambda A$ which is never invertible. Thus (i) of Theorem 1 is independent of whether $\lambda A + B$ is invertible.

<u>Example 6.2.3</u> Let $A = \begin{bmatrix} t & t^2 \\ 1 & t \end{bmatrix}$, $B = \begin{bmatrix} 1 & t \\ 0 & 0 \end{bmatrix}$. Then $B + \lambda A - \dot{A}$ is always singular. Thus by Theorem 1, the equation $A\dot{\underline{x}} + B\underline{x} = \underline{0}$ cannot be transformed to (1) by a transformation $\underline{x} = L\underline{y}$. Let $G = \begin{bmatrix} 0 & 1 \\ 1 & -t \end{bmatrix}$. Then multiplying $A\dot{\underline{x}} + B\underline{x} = \underline{0}$ by G gives $\tilde{A}\dot{\underline{x}} + \tilde{B}\underline{x} = \underline{0}$ where $\tilde{A} = \begin{bmatrix} 1 & t \\ 0 & 0 \end{bmatrix}$, $\tilde{B} = \begin{bmatrix} 0 & 0 \\ 1 & t \end{bmatrix}$ which is the equation in Example 1. Thus one can sometimes change to an equation of the required form by left multiplication by an invertible matrix G.

To date we have been unable to find a reasonably easy way to determine from A,B when there is a G so that $GA\dot{\underline{x}} + GB\underline{x} = \underline{0}$ satisfies (i), (ii) of Theorem 1.

3. <u>REDUCTION OF $A\dot{\underline{x}} + B\underline{x} = \underline{f}$ TO $\hat{A}\dot{\underline{x}} + \underline{x} = \hat{\underline{f}}$</u>

If the system cannot be reduced to constant coefficients as discussed in Section 2, then we shall show how to reduce the order of the system.

Analagous to the situation in Chapter 3, it is helpful to first put the system in a standard form.

This section is concerned with reducing, under suitable hypothesis, the system $A\dot{\underline{x}} + B\underline{x} = \underline{f}$ to the form $\hat{A}\dot{\underline{x}} + \underline{x} = \hat{\underline{f}}$. [A,B] in what follows in an $n \times 2n$ matrix and never $AB - BA$.

It will turn out that rank ([A,B]) = n is a natural condition to work with. But before showing why we need a fact from linear algebra.

<u>Proposition 6.3.1</u> Suppose that A,B are $n \times n$ matrices. Then the following are equivalent.

(i) $\mathcal{R}(A) + \mathcal{R}(B) = \mathbb{C}^n$,

(ii) $\text{rank}([A,B]) = n$

(iii) $AQ + B$ is invertible for some $Q \in \mathbb{C}^{n\times n}$.

<u>Proof</u> Clearly (i) and (ii) are equivalent, and (iii) implies (i) and (ii). Suppose then that (ii) holds. Let $\{\underline{e}_1, \ldots, \underline{e}_m\}$ be a basis for $\mathcal{R}(B^*) = \mathcal{N}(B)^{\perp}$ and $\{\underline{e}_{m+1}, \ldots, \underline{e}_n\}$ a basis for $\mathcal{N}(B)$. Now $\{B\underline{e}_1, \ldots, B\underline{e}_m\}$ is a basis for $\mathcal{R}(B)$. Pick $\underline{g}_{m+1}, \ldots, \underline{g}_n \in \mathcal{R}(A)$ so that $\{B\underline{e}_1, \ldots, B\underline{e}_m, \underline{g}_{m+1}, \ldots, \underline{g}_n\}$ is a basis for $\mathbb{C}^n$. Define $Q\underline{e}_i = \underline{0}$ if $i \leq M$ and $Q\underline{e}_i = A^{\dagger}\underline{g}_i$ if $i > m$. Then $(AQ + B)\underline{e}_i = B\underline{e}_i$ if $i \leq m$ and $(AQ + B)\underline{e}_i = \underline{g}_i$ if $i > m$ so that $AQ + B$ is invertible. □

The assumption that rank ([A,B]) = n is substantially weaker than $\lambda A + B$ being invertible for some λ since no restrictions (other than dimension) are placed on $\mathcal{N}(A), \mathcal{N}(B)$.

Example 6.3.1 Let $A = \begin{bmatrix} 1 & 0 \\ 0 & 0 \end{bmatrix}$, $B = \begin{bmatrix} 1 & 0 \\ 1 & 0 \end{bmatrix}$. Then $\lambda A + B$ is singular for all λ but $AQ + B$ is invertible if $Q = \begin{bmatrix} 0 & 1 \\ 0 & 0 \end{bmatrix}$.

Theorem 6.3.1 Suppose that A,B are $\mathbb{C}^{n\times n}$ valued functions, defined on the interval I. Suppose also that rank $([A,B]) \equiv n$ and rank (B), rank (A) are constant. Let $Q(t)$ be such that $AQ + B$ is invertible. Define T by $\dot{T} = QT$, $T(t_o) = I$. Let $\underline{x} = T\underline{y}$. Then $A\dot{\underline{x}} + B\underline{x} = \underline{f}$ is equivalent to $A\dot{\underline{y}} + \underline{y} = \hat{\underline{f}}$ where $\hat{A} = (A\dot{T} + BT)^{-1}AT = T^{-1}(AQ + B)^{-1}AT$, $\hat{\underline{f}} = T^{-1}(AQ + B)^{-1}\underline{f}$. Conversely, if T is an invertible, differentiable matrix function so that $A\dot{\underline{x}} + B\underline{x} = \underline{f}$ becomes $\hat{A}\dot{\underline{y}} + \underline{y} = \underline{f}$ with $\hat{A},\hat{\underline{f}},Q$ as above, then rank $([A,B]) = n$.

Proof The only part of Theorem 1 that needs comment beyond referring to Proposition 1 is the smoothness of $Q(t)$. $\{\underline{e}_1, \ldots ,\underline{e}_m\}$can be taken as columns of $B^\dagger B$. The $\{\underline{e}_{m+1}, \ldots ,\underline{e}_n\}$ are columns of $I - B^\dagger B$. If rank (B) is constant, then $B^\dagger$ is as smooth as A is. [16] □

It, of course, is quite possible for there to exist a $Q(t)$ such that $AQ + B$ is invertible without either rank$(A(t))$ or rank$(B(t))$ being constant as the scalar example $Q = I$, $A = [1 - t]$, $B = [t]$ shows.

Note that if one is interested in local results, then one can take $Q(t) \equiv Q(0)$ since $\det(A(0)Q(0) + B(0)) \neq 0$ implies $\det(A(t)Q(0) + B(t)) \neq 0$ in a neighborhood of zero.

As a special case of Theorem 1, we have

Corollary 6.3.1 If $\lambda(t)A(t) + B(t)$ is invertible on the interval I and λ is continuous, then $A\dot{\underline{x}} + B\underline{x} = \underline{f}$ may be rewritten as $\hat{A}\dot{\underline{y}} + \underline{y} = \hat{\underline{f}}$, $\hat{A} = (\lambda A + B)^{-1}A$, by the change of variables $\underline{x} = \exp(\int_0^t \lambda(s)ds)\underline{y}$.

In what follows we shall assume that the system has been written as $\hat{A}\dot{\underline{x}} + \underline{x} = \hat{\underline{f}}$.

4. $\hat{A}$ OF CONSTANT RANK, - REDUCTION METHODS

For this section we shall consider $\hat{A}\dot{\underline{x}} + \underline{x} = \hat{\underline{f}}$ where rank($\hat{A}$) is constant. The range of $\hat{A}$ is not assumed constant. We assume, for convenience, that $t_o = 0$. Our first approach is essentially that of Luenberger [51][52] with minor modification.

By taking a time invariant similarity, consisting of a permutation of the variables we may assume $\hat{A}(t) = \begin{bmatrix} A_1(t) & A_2(t) \\ A_3(t) & A_4(t) \end{bmatrix}$, rank($[A_1(t), A_2(t)]$) = rank($\hat{A}$), and $[A_1(t), A_2(t)]$ is of full row rank. Hence there exists a C(t), as smooth as the $A_i(t)$, such that $\hat{A}(t) = \begin{bmatrix} A_1 & A_2 \\ CA_1 & CA_2 \end{bmatrix}$. Thus $\hat{A}\dot{\underline{x}} + \underline{x} = \hat{\underline{f}}$ becomes

$$A_1\dot{\underline{x}}_1 + A_2\dot{\underline{x}}_2 + \underline{x}_1 = \underline{f}_1 , \tag{1}$$

$$CA_1\dot{\underline{x}}_1 + CA_2\dot{\underline{x}}_2 + \underline{x}_2 = \underline{f}_2 , \tag{2}$$

Multiplying (1) by -C and adding to (2) gives

$$-C\underline{x}_1 + \underline{x}_2 = \underline{f}_2 - C\underline{f}_1 \tag{3}$$

Using (3) to solve for $\underline{x}_2$ and substituting into (1), gives

$$A_1\dot{\underline{x}}_1 + A_2(\dot{C}\underline{x}_1 + C\dot{\underline{x}}_1 + \dot{\underline{f}}_2 - \dot{C}\underline{f}_1 - C\dot{\underline{f}}_1) + \underline{x}_1 = \underline{f}_1 \text{ or}$$

$$[A_1 + A_2C]\dot{\underline{x}}_1 + [A_2\dot{C} + I]\underline{x}_1 = \underline{f}_1 - A_2\dot{\underline{f}}_2 + A_2(C\dot{\underline{f}}_1 + \dot{C}\underline{f}_1). \tag{4}$$

Thus the original system has been reduced to one of lower order equal to rank([A,B]).

Clearly, in general, $A_1 + A_2C$ may be singular, in which case, the process may be repeated again provided $[[A_1 + A_2C], [A_2\dot{C} + I]]$ has full row rank so that Theorem 3.1 may be applied again. However, in many cases $A_1 + A_2C$ will be nonsingular.

Proposition 6.4.1 $A_1 + A_2C$ is invertible for t in some interval [0,b] if and only if $\mathrm{Ind}(\hat{A}(0)) = 1$.

Proof Note that $\begin{bmatrix} I & 0 \\ -C & I \end{bmatrix}\begin{bmatrix} A_1 & A_2 \\ CA_1 & CA_2 \end{bmatrix}\begin{bmatrix} I & 0 \\ C & I \end{bmatrix} = \begin{bmatrix} A_1+A_2C & A_2 \\ 0 & 0 \end{bmatrix}$. Since $[A_1 + A_2C, A_2]$ is of full row rank, A will be of index 1 if and only if $A_1 + A_2C$ is invertible. □

In certain special cases the invertibility of $A_1 + A_2C$ is completely determined by A_1.

Proposition 6.4.2 Suppose $\hat{A} = \begin{bmatrix} A_1 & A_2 \\ CA_1 & CA_2 \end{bmatrix}$ on [0,b]. If A is hermitian, then $A_1 + A_2C$ is invertible if and only if A_1 is.

Proof Suppose $\hat{A}$ is hermitian. Then $A_2 = A_1^*C^* = A_1C^*$. Hence $A_1 + A_2C = A_1 + A_1C^*C = A_1(I + C^*C)$. But $I + C^*C$ is invertible and Proposition 2 follows. □

We also note that many of our statements can be translated from statements about blocks to statements about the original matrix by replacing "$A_1 + A_2C$ is invertible" by "rank $(\hat{A}_1 + \hat{A}_2\hat{C}) = \mathrm{rank}\ (\hat{A}(0))$," and "$A_1$ is invertible" by "rank $(\hat{A}_1) = \mathrm{rank}\ (\hat{A}(0))$."

If it should happen that $[A_1 + A_2C, A_2\dot{C} + I]$ does not have constant rank, then one will probably have to deal with a Type II problem.

Luenberger does not first put the system $A\dot{\underline{x}} + B\underline{x} = \underline{f}$ in the form $\hat{A}\dot{\underline{x}} + \underline{x} = \hat{\underline{f}}$. However, his approach may lead to a much more complicated version of (3). Suppose rank(A) is constant and we operate on A,B instead of $\hat{A}$ to get

$$\begin{bmatrix} C_1 & C_2 \\ 0 & 0 \end{bmatrix}\begin{bmatrix} \dot{\underline{x}}_1 \\ \dot{\underline{x}}_2 \end{bmatrix} + \begin{bmatrix} B_1 & B_2 \\ B_3 & B_4 \end{bmatrix}\begin{bmatrix} \underline{x}_1 \\ \underline{x}_2 \end{bmatrix} = \begin{bmatrix} \tilde{\underline{f}}_1 \\ \tilde{\underline{f}}_2 \end{bmatrix}.$$

Then we have $B_3\underline{x}_1 + B_4\underline{x}_2 = \tilde{\underline{f}}_2$ which is much more difficult to work with than (3) unless B_4 is invertible.

The preceeding approaches use $\text{rank}(\hat{A})$ or $\text{rank}(A)$ constant. However, it's not just that rank of $\hat{A}$ is constant that is important, but also the behavior of the Jordan form of $\hat{A}$.

<u>Example 6.4.1</u> Let $\hat{A}(t) = \begin{bmatrix} t & 1 \\ 0 & 0 \end{bmatrix}$. Then $\text{rank}(A) \equiv 1$ but there is an index change at $t = 0$. The solution of $\hat{A}\dot{\underline{x}} - \underline{x} = \underline{0}$ is $\underline{x}(t) = \begin{bmatrix} \ln|t|x_o \\ 0 \end{bmatrix}$ which has an essential singularity at zero.

Thus Type II behavior can occur not only at rank changes of A but also at index changes. We shall now point out another way to reduce a systems order. While more cumbersome in that it involves more than just elementary row operations, it sometimes works better than the first method.

Let $T(t) \in \mathbb{C}^{n\times n}$ be such that $T^{-1}\hat{A}T = \begin{bmatrix} C_1 & C_2 \\ 0 & 0 \end{bmatrix}$, where $\mathbb{C}_1 \in \mathbb{C}^{r\times r}$, $C_2 \in \mathbb{C}^{r\times n-r}$. We assume that T is differentiable. Such a T requires only the existence of n-r pointwise linearly independent, differentiable vector valued functions $\underline{b}_1,\ldots,\underline{b}_{n-r}$ such that $\underline{b}_i(t) \in N(\hat{A}^*(t))$. The $\underline{b}_i(t)$ are the last n-r rows of T^{-1}. In particular, they will exist if $\text{rank}(\hat{A})$ is constant though it is not necessary.

Let $\underline{x} = T\begin{bmatrix} \underline{z} \\ \underline{w} \end{bmatrix}$, $\underline{z} \in \mathbb{C}^r$, $\underline{w} \in \mathbb{C}^{n-r}$. Then $\hat{A}\dot{\underline{x}} + \underline{x} = \hat{\underline{f}}$ becomes

$$\begin{bmatrix} C_1 & C_2 \\ 0 & 0 \end{bmatrix}\begin{bmatrix} \dot{\underline{z}} \\ \dot{\underline{w}} \end{bmatrix} + \left(I + \begin{bmatrix} C_1 & C_2 \\ 0 & 0 \end{bmatrix} (T^{-1}\dot{T}) \right)\begin{bmatrix} \underline{z} \\ \underline{w} \end{bmatrix} = \underline{T}^{-1}\hat{\underline{f}} = \begin{bmatrix} \underline{f}_1 \\ \underline{f}_2 \end{bmatrix}. \quad (5)$$

Thus $\underline{w} = \underline{f}_2$ and

$$C_1\dot{\underline{z}} + (I + C_1R_{11} + C_2R_{21})\underline{z} = \underline{f}_1 - (C_1R_{12} + C_2R_{22})\underline{f}_2 - C_2\dot{\underline{f}}_2 \tag{6}$$

where $T^{-1}\dot{T} = \begin{bmatrix} R_{11} & R_{12} \\ R_{21} & R_{22} \end{bmatrix}$. Note that (6) has order n-r.

It is instructive to consider an example that illustrates many of the difficulties with these problems. Let $Q(t)$ be a real analytic 3×3 matrix valued function. Define T by $\dot{T} = TQ$, $T(0) = I$. Thus T is also real analytic and invertible for all t. Let $A = T^{-1}NT$ where N is a 3×3 nilpotent Jordan block. Thus the rank, index, and Jordan form of A are all constant.

Let $\underline{x} = T\underline{y}$. Then $A\dot{\underline{x}} + \underline{x} = \underline{0}$ becomes $N\dot{\underline{y}} + (I + NQ)\underline{y} = \underline{0}$, (which is (5))

$$\begin{bmatrix} 0 & 1 & 0 \\ 0 & 0 & 1 \\ 0 & 0 & 0 \end{bmatrix}\begin{bmatrix} \dot{y}_1 \\ \dot{y}_2 \\ \dot{y}_3 \end{bmatrix} + \begin{bmatrix} 1 + q_{21} & q_{22} & q_{23} \\ q_{31} & 1 + q_{32} & q_{33} \\ 0 & 0 & 1 \end{bmatrix}\begin{bmatrix} y_1 \\ y_2 \\ y_3 \end{bmatrix} = \underline{0}.$$

Thus $y_3 = 0$ and the reduced system (6) is

$$\begin{bmatrix} 0 & 1 \\ 0 & 0 \end{bmatrix}\begin{bmatrix} \dot{y}_1 \\ \dot{y}_2 \end{bmatrix} + \begin{bmatrix} 1 + q_{21} & q_{22} \\ q_{31} & 1 + q_{32} \end{bmatrix}\begin{bmatrix} y_1 \\ y_2 \end{bmatrix} = \underline{0}.$$

Notice that the values of the q_{ij} are not restricted in any way, other than as to **smoothness**.

There are three possibilities.

(i) $q_{31} = 0$, $1 + q_{32} = 0$, in which case y_1 is arbitrary and y_2 is determined by $\dot{y}_2 + (1 + q_{21})y_1 + q_{22}y_{22} = 0$.

(ii) $q_{31} = 0$, $1 + q_{32} \neq 0$ almost everywhere, in which case $y_2 = 0$ and y_1 is either arbitrary or zero depending on $1 + q_{21}$.

(iii) $q_{31} \neq 0$, if which case $y_1 = -(1 + q_{32})(q_{31})^{-1}y_2$ and y_2 is determined by $\dot{y}_2 + [q_{22} - (1 + q_{21})(1 + q_{32})(q_{31})^{-1}y_2] = 0$

Note that q_{31} may have zeros in which case (iii) is a Type II problem when written as $q_{31}\dot{y}_2 + [q_{31}q_{22} - (1 + q_{21})(1 + q_{32})]y_2 = 0$.

Thus even if one starts with A analytic, constant Jordan form, etc., on some interval I, one should not be surprised if the procedures outlined earlier lead to solutions on properly smaller sub-intervals.

A complete analysis then of $\hat{A}\dot{\underline{x}} + \underline{x} = \underline{f}$ will involve not only the Jordan connical form of $\hat{A}$ but also the structure of $Q = T^{-1}\dot{T}$ where T is the similarity matrix.

The next proposition, while of limited applicability, does point out some interesting types of behavior.

Proposition 6.4.3 If $N^2 = 0$, then $\underline{x}$ is a solution of $N\dot{\underline{x}} + \underline{x} = \underline{f}$ if and only if $\underline{x}$ is a solution of the algebraic system of equations,

$$N\underline{x} = N\underline{f}, \tag{7}$$

$$(\dot{N} - I)\underline{x} = -\underline{f} + \dot{N}\underline{f} + N\dot{\underline{f}}. \tag{8}$$

Proof Suppose that $N\dot{\underline{x}} + \underline{x} = \underline{f}$ and $N^2 = 0$. Then $N\underline{x} = N\underline{f}$ and (7) holds. Differentiating (7) gives

$$\dot{N}\underline{x} + N\dot{\underline{x}} = \dot{N}\underline{f} + N\dot{\underline{f}} \tag{9}$$

or $N\dot{\underline{x}} - \underline{x} + \underline{f} = \dot{N}\underline{f} + N\dot{\underline{f}}$ and (8) follows. Conversely, suppose (7), (8) hold. Then (9) holds. Subtracting (8) from (9) gives $N\dot{\underline{x}} + \underline{x} = \underline{f}$ as desired. □

One curious consequence of Proposition 3 is that if $N^2 = 0$, then either $\dot{N}\underline{x} + \underline{x} = \underline{0}$ has only the zero solution just like when N is constant, or solutions may be multiplied by an arbitrary scalar function.

Example 6.4.2 Let $N = \begin{bmatrix} t & -1 \\ t^2 & -t \end{bmatrix}$. Then $\underline{x} = \phi(t)\begin{bmatrix} 1 \\ t \end{bmatrix}$ satisfies $N\underline{x} = \underline{0}$, $(I - \dot{N})\underline{x} = \underline{0}$.

Example 6.4.3 Let $N = \begin{bmatrix} t & t^2 \\ -1 & -t \end{bmatrix}$. Then $\mathcal{N}(N)$ is spanned by $\begin{bmatrix} t \\ 1 \end{bmatrix}$ while $\mathcal{N}(I - \dot{N})$ is spanned by $\begin{bmatrix} 1 \\ 0 \end{bmatrix}$. Hence $N\dot{\underline{x}} + \underline{x} = \underline{0}$ has only the zero solution.

Note that the N of Example 3 is just the transpose of the N of Example 2.

It is easy to determine when a solution of $A\dot{\underline{x}} + \underline{x} = \underline{0}$ may be multiplied by a scalar function and still be a solution.

Proposition 6.4.4 Suppose $\underline{x}$ is a solution of $A\dot{\underline{x}} + \underline{x} = \underline{0}$ on [a,b]. Then $\phi\underline{x}$ is also a solution for some $\phi \in C^1[a,b]$ such that $\phi \neq 0$ almost everywhere if and only if $\underline{x}$ is a solution of the algebraic system

$$A\underline{x} = \underline{0}, \qquad (I - \dot{A})\underline{x} = \underline{0} \tag{10}$$

Proof Clearly if $\underline{x}$ satisfies (10) so does $\phi\underline{x}$, and if $\underline{x}$ satisfies (10), then $\underline{x}$ is a solution of $A\dot{\underline{x}} + \underline{x} = \underline{0}$. On the other hand, if $\underline{x}$, $\phi\underline{x}$ satisfy $A\dot{\underline{x}} + \underline{x} = \underline{0}$, then $A\dot{\underline{x}} + \underline{x} = \underline{0}$ and $A(\phi\dot{\underline{x}} + \dot{\phi}\underline{x}) + \phi\underline{x} = \underline{0}$. Hence $\dot{\phi}A\underline{x} = \underline{0}$, so that $A\underline{x} = \underline{0}$. Thus $\dot{A}\underline{x} + A\dot{\underline{x}} = \underline{0}$ and (10) follows. □

We close this section with two final examples.

Example 6.4.4 Let $N(t) = \begin{bmatrix} t & 1 & 0 \\ 0 & 0 & 1 \\ -t^3 & -t^2 & -t \end{bmatrix}$. Note that $N(t) = L^{-1}\tilde{N}L$ where $L = \begin{bmatrix} 1 & 0 & 0 \\ t & 1 & 0 \\ t^2 & t & 1 \end{bmatrix}$, $L^{-1} = \begin{bmatrix} 1 & 0 & 0 \\ -t & 1 & 0 \\ 0 & -t & 1 \end{bmatrix}$, $\tilde{N} = \begin{bmatrix} 0 & 1 & 0 \\ 0 & 0 & 1 \\ 0 & 0 & 0 \end{bmatrix}$. Thus N is nilpotent of index 3 for all t and has constant rank. There are no nontrivial solutions of (10). However, the solution of $N\dot{\underline{x}} + \underline{x} = \underline{0}$ is $x_1 \equiv 0$, $x_2 = x_2(0)$, $x_3 = -tx_2(0)$. Thus solutions are uniquely determined by consistent initial conditions.

Example 6.4.5 Let $N(t) = \begin{bmatrix} t & 0 & -t^3 \\ 1 & 0 & -t^2 \\ 0 & 1 & -t \end{bmatrix}$. Note that this N is just the transpose of the one in Example 5. Then all solutions of $N\dot{\underline{x}} + \underline{x} = \underline{0}$ are of the form $\underline{x}(t) = C[t^5, t^4, 2t^3]^T$, C an arbitrary constant. Note that solutions to consistent initial conditions are not uniquely determined by the initial conditions at $t = 0$, though they are for $t \neq 0$.

5. NON-AUTONOMOUS DISCRETE SYSTEMS

Of course, in many applications involving discrete systems the coefficients may be non-autonomous. For example in the Leslie population model of Section 2.4, the birth and death rates may be time dependent. Similarly, the "output" matrix of the Leontief model in Section 2.5 is often time dependent.

Consider, then

$$A_k\underline{x}_{k+1} + B_k\underline{x}_k = \underline{f}_k, \quad k \geq 0, \tag{1}$$

where $A_k, B_k \in \mathbb{C}^{n\times n}$ and $\underline{f}_k$ is given.

The method presented here is a slight extension of that employed by Luenberger [51], [52] for "causal" systems.

Assume that $\text{rank}(A_k) = r$ is constant. (This is a discrete Type I assumption.) Then multiplication by an invertible P_k, (performing elementary row operations) gives

$$\begin{bmatrix} T_k \\ 0 \end{bmatrix}\underline{x}_{k+1} + \begin{bmatrix} C_k \\ D_k \end{bmatrix}\underline{x}_k = \begin{bmatrix} \underline{g}_k \\ \underline{h}_k \end{bmatrix} \tag{2}$$

where $\text{rank}(T_k) \equiv r$, $T_k \in \mathbb{C}^{r\times n}$. Now (2) may be rewritten as

$$\begin{bmatrix} T_k \\ D_{k+1} \end{bmatrix} \underline{x}_{k+1} + \begin{bmatrix} C_k \\ 0 \end{bmatrix} \underline{x}_k = \begin{bmatrix} \underline{g}_k \\ \underline{h}_{k+1} \end{bmatrix} \tag{3}$$

There are four possibilities.

Case I. $\begin{bmatrix} T_k \\ D_{k+1} \end{bmatrix}$ is invertible in which case we have what Luenberger calls a regular problem. In this case $\underline{x}_{k+1}$ is determined by $\underline{x}_k$, $\underline{f}_k$ and $\underline{f}_{k+1}$ as

$$\underline{x}_{k+1} = \begin{bmatrix} T_k \\ D_{k+1} \end{bmatrix}^{-1} \begin{bmatrix} \underline{g}_k \\ \underline{h}_{k+1} \end{bmatrix} - \begin{bmatrix} T_k \\ D_{k+1} \end{bmatrix}^{-1} \begin{bmatrix} C_k \\ 0 \end{bmatrix} \underline{x}_k .$$

Case II. Rank $\begin{bmatrix} T_k \\ D_{k+1} \end{bmatrix}$ is constant and greater than r. In this case (3) is viewed as (1) and a new (2) is computed with a T_k of rank greater than r.

Case III. Rank $\begin{bmatrix} T_k \\ D_{k+1} \end{bmatrix}$ is not constant and we have a discrete Type II problem.

Case IV. Rank $\begin{bmatrix} T_k \\ D_{k+1} \end{bmatrix}$ = Rank(T_k) for all k.

To discuss Case IV we need a variant of (2). Since rank$(T_k) \equiv r$, there exists invertible $P_{k+1} \in \mathbb{C}^{n\times n}$ such that $\begin{bmatrix} T_k \\ 0 \end{bmatrix} P_{k+1} = \begin{bmatrix} \Sigma_k & 0 \\ 0 & 0 \end{bmatrix}$ where $\Sigma_k \in \mathbb{C}^{r\times n}$ and Σ_k is invertible. Of course, P_{k+1} amounts to doing elementary column operations and Σ_k could be taken as the identity which we shall for simplicity.

Let $\underline{x}_k = P_k \underline{y}_k$ and $\underline{y}_k = \begin{bmatrix} \underline{z}_k \\ \underline{w}_k \end{bmatrix}$ where $\underline{z}_k \in \mathbb{C}^r$. Then (2) becomes

$$\begin{bmatrix} I & 0 \\ 0 & 0 \end{bmatrix} \begin{bmatrix} \underline{z}_{k+1} \\ \underline{w}_{k+1} \end{bmatrix} + \begin{bmatrix} L_k & M_k \\ N_k & R_k \end{bmatrix} \begin{bmatrix} \underline{z}_k \\ \underline{w}_k \end{bmatrix} = \begin{bmatrix} \underline{g}_k \\ \underline{h}_k \end{bmatrix}. \tag{4}$$

Now consider Cases I - IV. The only way Case IV could occur would be if $R_k \equiv 0$. Suppose that $R_k \equiv 0$, so that (4) is

$$\underline{z}_{k+1} + L_k\underline{z}_k + M_k\underline{w}_k = \underline{g}_k \tag{5}$$

$$N_k\underline{z}_k = \underline{h}_k \ . \tag{6}$$

If $N_k = 0$, then (5) provides the solution with $\underline{w}_k$ arbitrary. If N_k is one to one, then $\underline{z}_k = N_k^{\dagger}\underline{h}_k$ if (6) is consistent and (5) becomes an algebraic equation for $\underline{w}_k$ which may or may not be consistent depending on M_k and $\underline{h}_k$.

Suppose then N_k is not one to one. Then the only way a repetition of (3) can fail to increase the rank eventually is if $N_{k+1}M_k = 0$ and $N_{k+\ell}L_{k+\ell-1} \cdots L_{k+1}M_k = 0$ for $k \geq 0$, $\ell \geq 2$. For this very special case there are a large number of possibilities. Their enumeration is probably not particularly helpful, and problems of this type are probably best handled on an individual basis.

7 Computation

The preceding chapters have provided a variety of explicit formula for solving a variety of singular systems. While these results are quite useful in describing solutions and their behavior, they are not necessarily the quickest or most economical way to compute the solutions. As to be expected, however, they do suggest a way to compute the solutions.

In [16] we proposed a "deflation" algorithm for computing A^D using unitary operations as well as several other methods if A is "well-conditioned." Wilkinson in [66] also proposes a deflation method quite similar to ours but using similarity transformations. A somewhat related approach is used in a proof in [24].

It is obvious that to just compute a quantity like $A^{-1}\underline{b}$, or $A^{\dagger}\underline{b}$ one need not first compute A^{-1} or $A^{\dagger}$. Similarily, in [66], Wilkinson observes that, in fact, one may apply his deflation method directly to $A\dot{\underline{x}} + B\underline{x} = \underline{f}$ and obtain the solution without having to compute $[(\lambda A + B)^{-1}A]^D$ first.

This chapter will be concerned with solving

$$A\dot{\underline{x}} + B\underline{x} = \underline{f},\ A,B \in \mathbb{C}^{n\times n}. \tag{1}$$

In order to motivate this algorithm, let us first recall how (1) is solved in Chapter 3. If $\lambda A + B$ is invertible, then (1) is equivalent to

$$(\lambda A + B)^{-1}A\dot{\underline{x}} + (\lambda A + B)^{-1}B\underline{x} = (\lambda A + B)^{-1}\underline{f} \tag{2}$$

Let T be invertible so that $T(\lambda A + B)^{-1}AT^{-1} = \begin{bmatrix} C & 0 \\ 0 & N \end{bmatrix}$, where C is invertible and N is an upper-triangular nilpotent matrix. Since $(\lambda A + B)^{-1}B =$

$I - \lambda(\lambda A + B)^{-1}A$, (2) is equivalent to

$$\begin{bmatrix} C & 0 \\ 0 & N \end{bmatrix} (T\dot{\underline{x}}) + \begin{bmatrix} I-\lambda C & 0 \\ 0 & I-\lambda N \end{bmatrix} (T\underline{x}) = T(\lambda A + B)^{-1}\underline{f} .$$

Now the system (3) decouples into two systems. The first is a conventional nonsingular system and the second system is $N\dot{\underline{z}} + (I - \lambda N)\underline{z} = \underline{g}$ which we know from Theorem 3.2.3 to have a unique solution in terms of the derivatives of $\underline{g}$.

But the reduction of (1) to (3) can also be viewed as a change of variables $\underline{y} = T\underline{x}$, and a left multiplication by $P = T(\lambda A + B)^{-1}$ to change (1) into (here $Q = T^{-1}$)

$$PAQ\dot{\underline{y}} + PBQ\underline{y} = P\underline{f} \tag{4}$$

where $PAQ = \begin{bmatrix} C & 0 \\ 0 & N \end{bmatrix}$, $PBQ = \begin{bmatrix} I-\lambda C & 0 \\ 0 & I-\lambda N \end{bmatrix}$. Thus the reduction to (3) can be thought of as being accomplished by elementary row and column operations performed simultaneously on A,B and $\underline{f}$.

We shall show how Wilkinson arranged these operations into a reasonably efficient algorithm for solving (1). We shall concern ourself only with the case where the matrices involved are reasonably well conditioned and the rank, when needed, can be numerically determined. This is frequently the case in practice.

We shall also assume that $\lambda A + B$ is invertible for some λ. This is not necessary to start the algorithm. However, if $\lambda A + B$ is singular, the algorithm will eventually indicate that fact and not provide a complete solution.

If A is invertible, then $\dot{\underline{x}} + A^{-1}B\underline{x} = A^{-1}\underline{f}$ and (1) can be solved by classical means. So assume that A is singular. Then there is a sequence of elementary row operations given by a matrix P so that $PA = \begin{bmatrix} E \\ 0 \end{bmatrix}$, where E is of full row rank. Let $PB = \begin{bmatrix} F \\ G \end{bmatrix}$. Since $\begin{bmatrix} \lambda E+F \\ G \end{bmatrix}$ is invertible for some λ, G must be of full row rank. Thus there are elementary column operations Q so that $\begin{bmatrix} F \\ G \end{bmatrix} Q = \begin{bmatrix} B_1 & B_2 \\ 0 & B_3 \end{bmatrix}$, where B_3 is invertible and $\operatorname{rank}(B_3) = \operatorname{rank}(G)$. Let $\begin{bmatrix} E \\ 0 \end{bmatrix} Q = \begin{bmatrix} A_1 & A_2 \\ 0 & 0 \end{bmatrix}$. Then (4) becomes

$$\begin{bmatrix} A_1 & A_2 \\ 0 & 0 \end{bmatrix}\begin{bmatrix} \dot{\underline{x}}_1 \\ \dot{\underline{x}}_2 \end{bmatrix} + \begin{bmatrix} B_1 & B_2 \\ 0 & B_3 \end{bmatrix}\begin{bmatrix} \underline{x}_1 \\ \underline{x}_2 \end{bmatrix} = \begin{bmatrix} \underline{g}_1 \\ \underline{g}_2 \end{bmatrix}. \tag{5}$$

But B_3 is invertille. Hence $\underline{x}_2 = B_3^{-1}\underline{g}_2$ and

$$A_1\dot{\underline{x}}_1 + B_1\underline{x}_1 = \underline{g}_1 - A_2B_3^{-1}\dot{\underline{g}}_2 - B_2B_3^{-1}\underline{g}_2. \tag{6}$$

Now there are three possibilities. If A_1 is invertible, then (6) is solved classically. If $A_1 = 0$, then B_1 is invertible and (6) gives $\underline{x}_1$. If $A_1 \neq 0$ and A_1 is singular, then we repeat the process again on (6) to get a new system in the form of (5). Since the order of the system decreases at each iteration, the process terminates in a finite amount of time.

It goes without saying that in solving (5) for $\underline{x}_2$, one would not compute B_3^{-1} but rather solve $B_3\underline{x}_2 = \underline{g}_2$ by elementary row operations.

These same ideas can be applied to compute many of the other quantities in this book.

For example, if one just wanted to compute A^D, then again take $P_1A = \begin{bmatrix} E \\ 0 \end{bmatrix}$, $E \in \mathbb{C}^{r\times r}$ where E is of full row rank. Then $P_1AP_1^{-1} = \begin{bmatrix} E_1 & E_2 \\ 0 & 0 \end{bmatrix}$, $E_1 \in \mathbb{C}^{r\times r}$. If $E_1 = 0$ or is invertible we stop. If not, we repeat the process on E_1. Continuing in this way we eventually either get

$$P_k \cdots P_1 A P_1^{-1} \cdots P_k^{-1} = \left[\begin{array}{c|cccc} A_{11} & \cdot & \cdots & \cdot & A_{1,k+1} \\ \hline 0 & 0 & A_{23} & \cdots & A_{3,k+1} \\ \vdots & & \ddots & & \vdots \\ \vdots & & & \ddots & A_{k,k+1} \\ 0 & \cdot & \cdots & \cdot & 0 \end{array}\right] = \left[\begin{array}{c|c} A_{11} & C \\ \hline 0 & N \end{array}\right]$$

where A_{11} is invertible or just $\begin{bmatrix} 0 & A_{12} & \cdots & A_{1,k} \\ \vdots & & \ddots & A_{k-1,k} \\ 0 & \cdots & \cdots & 0 \end{bmatrix}$. In the second case $A^D = 0$. In the first case, k additional similarities are performed to annihilate A_{1i}, $1 < i < k+1$. In each case the similarity is the obvious one of using elementary column operations and the invertible A_{11}. For example, if $P = \begin{bmatrix} I & -A_{11}^{-1}A_{12} & \cdot & 0 \\ 0 & I & & \vdots \\ \vdots & & \ddots & \vdots \\ 0 & \cdots & \cdots & I \end{bmatrix}$,

$$P^{-1}P_k \cdots P_1 A P_1^{-1} \cdots P_k^{-1} P = \begin{bmatrix} A_{11} & 0 & A_{13} & \cdots & A_{1,k+1} \\ 0 & 0 & A_{23} & \cdots & A_{2,k+1} \\ \vdots & & & & \vdots \\ 0 & \cdots & \cdots & \cdots & 0 \end{bmatrix}. \qquad (8)$$

Depending on exactly what one wants to compute there is another way to proceed from (7) which, while mathematically equivalent to proceeding as in (8), is worth noting. Let X be the solution of

$$A_{11}X - XN = -C. \qquad (9)$$

If X is $r \times s$, then (9) is a linear system in rs variables. Since A_{11} is invertible and N is nilpotent, (9) has a unique solution. This system is well discussed in the literature. Let $X = [X_1, \ldots, X_k]$. Then from (7) we have (9) is

$$A_{11}X_1 = A_{12}$$
$$A_{11}X_2 - X_1A_{23} = A_{13} \tag{10}$$
$$A_{11}X_3 - X_1A_{24} - X_2A_{34} = A_{14},$$

One may solve the first equation in (10) for X_1, the second for X_2, and so on.

Suppose now that the solution X of (9) has been computed. Then $\begin{bmatrix} A_{11} & B \\ 0 & N \end{bmatrix} = \begin{bmatrix} I & X \\ 0 & I \end{bmatrix}\begin{bmatrix} A_{11} & 0 \\ 0 & N \end{bmatrix}\begin{bmatrix} I & -X \\ 0 & I \end{bmatrix}$. Hence $\begin{bmatrix} A_{11} & B \\ 0 & N \end{bmatrix}^D = \begin{bmatrix} A_{11}^{-1} & A_{11}^{-1}X \\ 0 & 0 \end{bmatrix}$ and $\begin{bmatrix} A_{11} & B \\ 0 & N \end{bmatrix}^D\begin{bmatrix} A_{11} & B \\ 0 & N \end{bmatrix} = \begin{bmatrix} I & -X \\ 0 & 0 \end{bmatrix}$. It is the use of (9) to compute X which makes the deflation algorithm of [66] superior to the other proposed deflation algorithms.

8 Higher order systems

1. BACKGROUND AND PROBLEMS

Up to this point we have been concerned entirely with first order systems. What of higher order systems? Do the ideas presented, so far, work for systems of the form

$$A_m\underline{x}^{(m)}(t) + A_{m-1}\underline{x}^{(m-1)}(t) + \ldots + A_1\underline{x}^{(1)}(t) + A_0\underline{x}(t) = \underline{f}(t) \tag{1}$$

where $A_i \in \mathbb{C}^{m\times n}$? Of course (1) may be written as a first order system by the standard trick of setting $\underline{y}_1 = \underline{x}^{(1)}$, $\underline{y}_2 = \underline{x}^{(2)}, \ldots, \underline{y}_{m-1} = \underline{x}^{(m-1)}$, so that (1) becomes

$$\begin{bmatrix} I & 0 & \cdots & 0 \\ 0 & I & & \vdots \\ & & \ddots & \vdots \\ 0 & \cdots & 0 & A_m \end{bmatrix} \dot{\begin{bmatrix} \underline{x}_1 \\ \underline{y}_1 \\ \vdots \\ \underline{y}_{m-1} \end{bmatrix}} + \begin{bmatrix} 0 & -I & 0 & \cdots & 0 \\ 0 & 0 & -I & \cdots & 0 \\ & & & \ddots & -I \\ A_0 & A_1 & \cdots & \cdots & A_{m-1} \end{bmatrix} \begin{bmatrix} \underline{x}_1 \\ \underline{y}_1 \\ \vdots \\ \underline{y}_{m-1} \end{bmatrix} = \begin{bmatrix} \underline{0} \\ \underline{0} \\ \vdots \\ \underline{f} \end{bmatrix} \tag{2}$$

or

$$\mathcal{A}\dot{\underline{z}} + \mathcal{B}\underline{z} = \underline{g}. \tag{3}$$

The system (2) is a singular system if and only if A_m is singular.

(1) has been considered by several authors. For example, Duffin [23], [24], Gohberg [29], and Langenhop [35], [47].

In principal, everything one would need to know about (1) can be found out from (2). However, it would be interesting to have an expression for the solutions of (1), or a description of their behavior, directly in terms of the A_i.

This chapter will present some of the background material on (1) and discuss what type of additional work is, in our opinion, needed. Let

$$A(\lambda) = \sum_{i=0}^{m} A_m \lambda^m. \tag{4}$$

Consistent with [28] we call (1) <u>regular</u> if (4) is invertible for some λ.

<u>Proposition 8.1.1</u> Solutions to (1) are uniquely determined by consistent initial conditions if and only if (1) is regular. If $\underline{f}$ is sufficiently differentiable, and (1) is regular, then (1) is consistent for some initial values $\underline{x}(0),\ldots,\underline{x}^{(m-1)}(0)$.

<u>Proof</u> It is possible to prove Proposition 1 directly from (1). However, the proof in [35] is probably quicker. Note that

$$\lambda\mathcal{A} + \mathcal{B} = \begin{bmatrix} 0 & -I & 0 \cdots & 0 \\ 0 & 0 & -I \cdots & 0 \\ \vdots & & & \vdots \\ 0 & 0 & \cdots & -I \\ A(\lambda) & C_1(\lambda) & \cdots & C_{m-1}(\lambda) \end{bmatrix} \begin{bmatrix} I & 0 & 0 \cdots & 0 & 0 \\ -\lambda I & I & 0 \cdots & 0 & 0 \\ 0 & -\lambda I & I \cdots & 0 & 0 \\ \vdots & & & \vdots & \vdots \\ 0 & 0 & 0 \cdots & -\lambda I & I \end{bmatrix}$$

where $C_i(\lambda) = \sum_{j=i}^{m} A_j \lambda^{j-i}$. Then $\det(\lambda\mathcal{A} + \mathcal{B}) = \det A(\lambda)$. Thus (1) is regular if and only if (2) is regular and Proposition 1 follows from Theorem 3.1.3 applied to (2). □

Now there are methods for solving (1) if (1) is regular. In [35] a method is given which consists of first finding the λ_i for which $A(\lambda_i)$ is singular and then generating a "complete set of singular sequences." While of mathematical interest, we find that approach not completely satisfactory on two counts.

First, if one had a particular (1) that one actually wanted to solve, the amount of work involved in this process is probably both more time consuming, and more numerically sensitive, than to just apply Wilkinson's algorithm of Chapter 7 directly to the system (2).

Secondly, this approach does not provide for closed form solutions for (1) directly in terms of the A_i. For the first order system $A\dot{\underline{x}} + B\underline{x} = \underline{0}$, we feel that there is something more satisfying about characterizing the space of initial conditions as $\mathcal{R}(\hat{A}^D\hat{A})$, $\hat{A} = (\lambda A + B)^{-1}A$, as opposed to the iterated set mapping $B^{-1}AB^{-1}\cdots AB^{-1}AB^{-1}\{\underline{0}\}$ found in [67] which is equivalent to the singular sequence of [35]. (Here B^{-1} means inverse image and not that B is invertible).

The development in [29] is similar to that of [35]. Although [29] develops an elaborate theory for matrix polynomials and contributes to our understanding of them, it also has the two shortcomings addressed above. Perhaps the approach of [29] is the best possible, for the case $m > 1$ we have been unable to do better. However, we believe the problem is worth further investigation.

We shall conclude this section by presenting a couple of specific problems we would like to see solved.

Consider (1), (4) with $m = 2$;

$$A\ddot{\underline{x}} + B\dot{\underline{x}} + C\underline{x} = \underline{f}, \quad A(\lambda) = \lambda^2 A + \lambda B + C \tag{5}$$

Equation (5) could naturally arise, for example, in considering electrical circuits. Let $\underline{y} = \dot{\underline{x}}$ so that (5) is

$$\begin{bmatrix} B & A \\ I & 0 \end{bmatrix}\begin{bmatrix} \dot{\underline{x}} \\ \dot{\underline{y}} \end{bmatrix} + \begin{bmatrix} C & 0 \\ 0 & -I \end{bmatrix}\begin{bmatrix} \underline{x} \\ \underline{y} \end{bmatrix} = \begin{bmatrix} \underline{f} \\ \underline{0} \end{bmatrix}. \tag{6}$$

Suppose that C were invertible. Then (6) would be

$$\begin{bmatrix} C^{-1}B & C^{-1}A \\ -I & 0 \end{bmatrix} \begin{bmatrix} \dot{\underline{x}} \\ \dot{\underline{y}} \end{bmatrix} + \begin{bmatrix} I & 0 \\ 0 & I \end{bmatrix} \begin{bmatrix} \underline{x} \\ \underline{y} \end{bmatrix} = \begin{bmatrix} C^{-1}\underline{f} \\ 0 \end{bmatrix}. \tag{7}$$

<u>Problem</u> Find a formula for $\begin{bmatrix} X & Y \\ I & 0 \end{bmatrix}^D$ in terms of X and Y.

The solution of this Problem would be of some interest as a contribution to the theory of generalized inverses. However, its real importance lies in providing solutions and information about (5). From the theory developed in Chapter 3, it is clear that the Problem is equivalent to solving (5) in terms of A,B,C and $\underline{f}$.

The assumption that C is invertible is actually not restrictive. For let λ be such that $A(\lambda)$ is invertible. Let $\underline{x} = e^{\lambda t}\underline{z}$. Then (5) becomes

$$A\ddot{\underline{z}} + (2\lambda A + B)\dot{\underline{z}} + A(\lambda)\underline{z} = e^{-\lambda t}\underline{f}, \tag{8}$$

and (8) is in the form (5) but with C invertible.

The Problem is also closely related to certain riccati equations. Since the Drazin inverse is well behaved with respect to similarity it is natural to try and make $\begin{bmatrix} X & Y \\ I & 0 \end{bmatrix}$ simpler by a similarity. The Drazin inverses of upper and lower triangular matrices are known [16].

Suppose one considered an invertible matrix $\begin{bmatrix} E & F \\ G & 0 \end{bmatrix}$ and asked when is $\begin{bmatrix} E & F \\ G & 0 \end{bmatrix} \begin{bmatrix} X & Y \\ I & 0 \end{bmatrix} \begin{bmatrix} E & F \\ G & 0 \end{bmatrix}^{-1}$ either upper or lower block triangular with the same size blocks. It is easy to verify that if $Y \neq 0$, this happens if and only if $EX + F - EYF^{-1}E = 0$. Letting $K = F^{-1}E$, we get

$$KX + I - KYK = 0 \tag{9}$$

which is a standard riccati equation. It is easy to check that the other choices of $\begin{bmatrix} 0 & E \\ F & G \end{bmatrix}$, $\begin{bmatrix} E & F \\ 0 & G \end{bmatrix}$, $\begin{bmatrix} E & 0 \\ F & G \end{bmatrix}$ all lead to equations similar to (9). Thus a complete solution of the Problem will tell when certain riccati equations have invertible solutions.

In some applications, such as electrical circuits, some, or all, of A,B,C often have a special form such as symmetric or positive semi-definite. It seems reasonable that in some of these special cases, the problem might be more easily resolved.

Finally, note that the two special cases $C = 0$, or $B = 0$ are easily solved. If $C = 0$, then $A\ddot{\underline{x}} + B\dot{\underline{x}} = \underline{f}$ is first order in $\dot{\underline{x}}$. It may be solved for $\dot{\underline{x}}$ using Theorem 3.1.3 and then antidifferentiating to give $\underline{x}$. If $B = 0$, we have $A\ddot{\underline{x}} + C\underline{x} = \underline{f}$. This equation is easily solved using Laplace transforms. One just takes $s^2 = \lambda$ in the Laurent expansion of $\lambda A + C$ given by Theorem 4.2.1.

2. SECOND ORDER SYSTEMS

The ideas of this section extend easily to higher than second order systems but for notational convenience, we shall limit our discussion to studying

$$A\ddot{\underline{z}} + B\dot{\underline{z}} + C\underline{z} = \underline{f}, \quad A,B \in \mathbb{C}^{n\times n}. \tag{1}$$

In [35], some results of Duffin [23] are extended to cover (1) when A,B,C are all real symmetric positive definite matrices. In this section we shall show how the approach of Luenberger described in Section 4.5 can be slightly modified to solve (1) under a wide variety of conditions.

Let E,F be invertible matrices so that $EAF = \begin{bmatrix} A_1 & 0 \\ 0 & 0 \end{bmatrix}$ with A_1 invertible. Let $\underline{w} = F^{-1}\underline{z} = \begin{bmatrix} \underline{x} \\ \underline{y} \end{bmatrix}$. Then (1) becomes

$$\begin{bmatrix} A_1 & 0 \\ 0 & 0 \end{bmatrix}\begin{bmatrix} \ddot{\underline{x}} \\ \ddot{\underline{y}} \end{bmatrix} + \begin{bmatrix} B_1 & B_2 \\ B_3 & B_4 \end{bmatrix}\begin{bmatrix} \dot{\underline{x}} \\ \dot{\underline{y}} \end{bmatrix} + \begin{bmatrix} C_1 & C_2 \\ C_3 & C_4 \end{bmatrix}\begin{bmatrix} \underline{x} \\ \underline{y} \end{bmatrix} = \begin{bmatrix} \underline{f} \\ \underline{g} \end{bmatrix}. \tag{2}$$

Differentiating the second line of (2) gives

$$\begin{bmatrix} A_1 & 0 \\ B_3 & B_4 \end{bmatrix}\begin{bmatrix} \ddot{\underline{x}} \\ \ddot{\underline{y}} \end{bmatrix} + \begin{bmatrix} B_1 & B_2 \\ C_3 & C_4 \end{bmatrix}\begin{bmatrix} \dot{\underline{x}} \\ \dot{\underline{y}} \end{bmatrix} + \begin{bmatrix} C_1 & C_2 \\ 0 & 0 \end{bmatrix}\begin{bmatrix} \underline{x} \\ \underline{y} \end{bmatrix} = \begin{bmatrix} \underline{f} \\ \dot{\underline{g}} \end{bmatrix} \tag{3}$$

Now if B_4 is invertible, (3) is a nonsingular system and a solution $\underline{x},\underline{y}$ exists for any $\underline{x}(0)$, $\underline{y}(0)$, $\dot{\underline{x}}(0)$, $\dot{\underline{y}}(0)$. Taking such a solution of (3), substituting it into (2), and using (3) we see that $\underline{x},\underline{y}$ is a solution of (2) if and only if

$$B_3\dot{\underline{x}}(0) + B_4\dot{\underline{y}}(0) + C_3\underline{x}(0) + C_4\underline{y}(0) = \underline{g}(0) \tag{4}$$

Let us call (1) <u>nonsingularizable</u> if there exists E,F so that in (2), B_4 is invertible. Recall that an EP matrix [16] is one such that $AA^{\dagger} = A^{\dagger}A$. All normal matrices are EP.

<u>Proposition 8.2.1</u> Both of the following imply that (1) is nonsingularizable:

(i) A is EP and B is positive definite.

(ii) A is EP, B is positive semi-definite, and $\lambda A + B$ is invertible for some λ.

In both these cases, the set of consistent initial conditions is characterized by

$$(I - A^{\dagger}A)B\dot{\underline{z}}(0) + (I - A^{\dagger}A)C\underline{z}(0) = (I - A^{\dagger}A)\underline{f}(0). \tag{5}$$

<u>Proof</u> Clearly the sufficiency of (ii) implies the sufficiency of (i). Suppose then (ii) holds. Take $E = U$, $F = U^*$ where $UAU^* = \begin{bmatrix} A_1 & 0 \\ 0 & 0 \end{bmatrix}$ and

A_1 is invertible. (The existence of such a U is equivalent to A being EP.) Suppose that B_4 were singular. Let $\underline{u}$ be such that $B_4\underline{u} = \underline{0}$. If $B_2\underline{u} = \underline{0}$, then $(\lambda A + B)U^*\underline{u} = \underline{0}$ for all λ which is a contradiction. Hence $B_2\underline{u} \neq 0$. Let $\underline{v} = \varepsilon B_2\underline{u}$. Then

$$\begin{bmatrix} \underline{v} \\ \underline{u} \end{bmatrix}^* \begin{bmatrix} B_1 & B_2 \\ B_2^* & B_4 \end{bmatrix} \begin{bmatrix} \underline{v} \\ \underline{u} \end{bmatrix} = \varepsilon^2 \underline{u}^* B_2^* B_1 B_2 \underline{u} + 2\varepsilon \underline{u}^* B_2^* B_2 \underline{u}.$$

But for $\varepsilon < 0$, $|\varepsilon|$ small, this expression is negative which contradicts the positive semi-definiteness of B. Hence B_4 is nonsingular. The characterization (5) now follows from the fact that $(UAU^*)^\dagger = UA^\dagger U^*$. □

Proposition 1 is nice because it is reasonably easy to verify (i) or (ii). However, there are many other ways to arrive at (2). If EAF provides the singular value decomposition of A, we get the following.

Proposition 8.2.2 If rank $((I - A^\dagger A)B(I - A^\dagger A)) = n - \text{rank}(A)$, then (1) is nonsingularizable and the set of consistent initial conditions is again characterized by (5).

If A has index one, it is easy to get a variation of Proposition 2 with rank $([B;A]) = n\text{-rank}(A)$ and $[I;A]B\dot{\underline{z}}(0) + [I;A]C\underline{z}(0) = [I;A]\underline{f}(0)$. We leave the details to the reader.

Note also that nonsingularizable is not only a stronger property than regularity but is even stronger than assuming that $\lambda A + B$ is invertible for some λ.

Proposition 8.2.3 If the system (2) is nonsingularizable and is written as a first order system in the form (1.6) and this system is denoted by $\mathcal{A}\dot{\underline{x}} + \mathcal{B}\underline{x} = \underline{h}$, then $\text{Ind}(\hat{\mathcal{A}}) = \text{Ind}((\lambda\mathcal{A} + \mathcal{B})^{-1}\mathcal{A}) = 1$.

Proof If (2) is nonsingularizable, we have

$$\mathcal{A} = \left[\begin{array}{ccc|c} B_1 & B_2 & A_1 & 0 \\ B_3 & B_4 & 0 & 0 \\ I & 0 & 0 & 0 \\ \hline 0 & I & 0 & 0 \end{array}\right] = \begin{bmatrix} \mathcal{A}_{11} & 0 \\ \mathcal{A}_{21} & 0 \end{bmatrix},$$

$$\mathcal{B} = \left[\begin{array}{ccc|c} C_1 & C_2 & 0 & 0 \\ C_3 & C_4 & 0 & 0 \\ 0 & 0 & -I & 0 \\ \hline 0 & 0 & 0 & -I \end{array}\right] = \begin{bmatrix} \mathcal{B}_{11} & 0 \\ 0 & -I \end{bmatrix}.$$

Note that $\mathcal{A}_{11}$ is invertible. Hence $\lambda\mathcal{A} + \mathcal{B}$ is invertible for some λ. But then

$$\hat{\mathcal{A}} = (\lambda\mathcal{A} + \mathcal{B})^{-1}\mathcal{A} = \begin{bmatrix} (\lambda\mathcal{A}_{11} + \mathcal{B}_{11})^{-1}\mathcal{A}_{11} & 0 \\ \lambda\mathcal{A}_{21}(\lambda\mathcal{A}_{11} + \mathcal{B}_{11})^{-1} & 0 \end{bmatrix}$$ which has index one. □

Proposition 3 is essentially the same as Proposition 3.6.2 except we have chosen a different method of proof.

References

1. M. Athens and P. L. Falb, Optimal Control, McGraw-Hill, New York, 1966.

2. D. J. Bell and D. H. Jacobson, Singular Optimal Control Problems, Academic Press, New York, 1975.

3. L. Berg, Solution of degenerate linear initial value problems, ZAMM 57, (1977), 65-73.

4. V. F. Butuzov and A. B. Vasiléva, Differential equation systems with a small parameter for the case in which the unperturbed (singular) system is in the spectrum, Diff. Eqn. 6(1970), 499-510.

5. S. L. Campbell, The Drazin inverse of an infinite matrix, SIAM J. Appl. Math. 31(1976), 492-503.

6. S. L. Campbell, Linear systems of differential equations with singular coefficients, SIAM J. Math. Anal. 8(1977), 1057-1066.

7. S. L. Campbell, On the limit of a product of matrix exponentials, Linear and Multilinear Alg. 6(1978), 55-59.

8. S. L. Campbell, Singular pertrubation of autonomous linear systems, II, J. Diff. Eqn., 29(1978), 362-373.

9. S. L. Campbell, Limit behavior of solutions of singular difference equations, Linear Alg. and Its Appl., 23(1979), 167-178.

10. S. L. Campbell, Optimal control of discrete linear processes with quadratic cost, International J. Systems Science, 9(1978), 841-847.

11. S. L. Campbell, Optimal control of autonomous linear processes with singular matrices in the quadratic cost functional, SIAM J. Control, 14(1976), 1092-1106.

12. S. L. Campbell, On a singularly perturbed autonomous linear control problem, IEEE Trans. Automatic Control AC-24, (1979), 115-116.

13. S. L. Campbell, Nonregular singular dynamic Leontief systems, Econometrica (to appear).

14. S. L. Campbell, Singular systems of differential equations with delays, preprint.

15. S. L. Campbell and C. D. Meyer, Jr., Recent applications of the Drazin inverse, Recent Applications of Generalized Inverses, Ed. M. Nashed, Pitman Publ. Co., 1979.

16. S. L. Campbell and C. D. Meyer, Jr., Generalized Inverses of Linear Transformations, Pitman Publishing Co., Ltd., 1979.

17. S. L. Campbell, C. D. Meyer, Jr., and N. J. Rose, Applications of the Drazin inverse to linear systems of differential equations, SIAM J. Appl. Math., 31(1976), 411-425.

18. S. L. Campbell and N. J. Rose, Singular perturbation of autonomous linear systems, SIAM J. Math. Anal., 10(1979), 542-551.

19. S. L. Campbell and N. J. Rose, Singular perturbation of autonomous linear systems III, Houston J. Math. 4(1978), 527-539.

20. R. V. Churchill, Operational mathematics, McGraw-Hill, New York, 1958.

21. R. H. Cole, Theory of Ordinary Differential Equations, Appleton-Century Crofts, New York, 1968.

22. J. E. Dennis, Jr., J. F. Traub and R. P. Weber, The algebraic theory of matrix polynomials, SIAM J. Numer. Anal. 13(1976), 831-845.

23. R. J. Duffin, A minimax theory for overdamped networks, J. Rat. Mech. and Anal. 4(1955), 221-223.

24. R. J. Duffin, Chrystal's theorem on differential equation systems, J. Math. Anal. and Appl. 8(1963), 325-331.

25. R. S. Ellis and M. A. Pinsky, Asymptotic nonuniqueness of the Navier-Stokes equations in kinetic theory, Bull. Amer. Math. Soc. 80(1974), 1160-1164.

26. R. S. Ellis and M. A. Pinsky, The projection of the Navier-Stokes equations upon the Euler equations, J. Math. Pures, Appl. 54(1975), 157-182.

27. A. Feingold and R. Varga, Block diagonally dominant matrices and generalizations of the Gerschgorin circle theorem, Pacific J. Math., 12(1962), 1241-1250.

28. F. R. Gantmacher, The Theory of Matrices, Volume II, Chelsea Publishing Company, New York, 1960.

29. I. Gohberg, M. A. Kaashoek, and L. Rodman, Common multiples and common divisors of matrix polynomials, I. Spectral method, preprint 1978.

30. W. A. Harris, Singular perturbation of two-point boundary value problems for systems of ordinary differential equations, Arch. Ration. Mech. Anal., 5(1960), 212-225.

31. W. A. Harris, Jr., Singular perturbations of two-point boundary value problems, J. Math. Mech., 11(1962), 371-382.

32. W. A. Harris, Jr., Singular perturbation of boundary value problems for a system of differential equations, Duke Math. J., 29(1962), 429-445.

33. W. A. Harris, Jr., Singularly perturbed boundary value problems revisited, Symposium on Ordinary Differential Equations, Lecture Notes in Mathematics, No. 312, Springer-Verlag, New York, 1972, 54-64.

34. P. Hartman, Ordinary Differential Equations, John Wiley & Sons, Inc., New York, 1964.

35. J. W. Hooker and C. E. Langenhop, On regular systems of linear differential equations with constant coefficients, preprint, 1979.

36. D. H. Jacobson, Totally singular quadratic minimization problems, IEEE Trans. Automatic Control, 16(1971), 651-657.

37. T. Kato, On a matrix limit theorem, Linear and Multilinear Alg. 3(1975), 67-71.

38. T. Kato, Perturbation Theory for Linear Operators, Springer-Verlag, New York, 1966.

39. T. G. Kemeny, J. Laurie Snell, and A. W. Knapp, Denumerable Markov Chains, D. Van Nostrand, Princeton, N. J., 1966.

40. D. Kendrick, On the Leontief dynamic inverse, Quarterly J. Economics, 86(1972), 693-696.

41. P. K. Kokotovic, Singular perturbations in optimal control, Rocky Mtn. J. Math. 6(1976), 767-773.

42. P. K. Kokotovic and P. Sannuti, Singular perturbation method for reducing the model order in optimal control design, IEEE Trans. Automatic Control, 13(1968), 377-384.

43. P. K. Kokotovic and R. A. Yuckel, Singular perturbation theory of linear state regulators, IEEE Trans. Automatic Control, 17(1972), 29-37.

44. R. G. Kreijger and H. Neudecker, Kendrick's 'forward integration method' and the dynamic Leontief multisectoral model, Quarterly J. Economics, 90(1976), 505-507.

45. G. A. Kurina, Asymptotic solution of a classical singularly perturbed optimal control problem, Soviet Math. Dokl. 18(1977), 722-726.

46. P. Lancaster, Theory of Matrices, Academic Press, New York, 1969.

47. C. E. Langenhop, The Laurent expansion of a nearly singular matrix, Linear Alg. and Its Appl. 4(1971), 329-340.

48. W. Leontief, et. al., Studies in the Structure of the American Economy, Oxford University Press, New York, 1953.

49. W. Leontief, Essays in Economics, M. E. Sharpe, Inc., N. Y., 1977.

50. D. A. Livesey, The singularity problem in the dynamic input-output model, International J. Systems Science, 4(1973), 437-440.

51. D. G. Luenberger, Dynamic equations in descriptor form, IEEE Trans. Automatic Control, Vol. AC-22 (1977), 312-321.

52. D. G. Luenberger, Time invariant descriptor systems, Proceedings 1977 Joint Automatic Control Conference, San Francisco, CA, 725-730.

53. D. G. Luenberger and A. Arbel, Singular dynamic Leontief systems, Econometrica, 45(1977), 991-995.

54. C. D. Meyer, Jr. and N. J. Rose, The index and the Drazin inverse of block triangular matrices, SIAM J. Appl. Math., 33(1976), 1-7.

55. M. J. Niccolai, The reachable set and an application to the solution of linear control systems with singular matrix coefficients, Ph.D. Thesis, North Carolina State University, 1976.

56. R. E. O'Malley, Jr. and A. Jameson, Singular perturbations and singular arcs - Part I, IEEE Trans. Automatic Control AC-20, 1975, 218-226.

57. R. E. O'Malley, Jr., Cheap control singular arcs, and singular perturbations, Lecture Notes in Economics and Mathematics Systems, No. 106, Springer-Verlag.

58. R. E. O'Malley, Jr. and J. E. Fhaherty, Singular singular-perturbation problems, Lecture Notes in Mathematics, No. 594, Springer-Verlag, 422-436.

59. A. Perold, Fundamentals of a continuous time simplex method, Technical Report SOL 78-26, Department of Operations Research, Stanford University, Stanford, CA., 1978.

60. B. Porter, Design of stabilizing feedback controllers for a class of multivariable linear systems with slow and fast modes, International J. Control, 23(1976), 49-54.

61. N. J. Rose, The Laurent expansion of a generalized resolvent with some applications, SIAM J. Math. Anal. 9(1978), 751-758.

62. A. B. Vasiléva, Singularly perturbed systems containing indeterminacy in the case of degeneracy. Soviet Math. Dokl. 16(1975), 1121-1125.

63. G. C. Verghese, Infinite-frequency behavior in generalized dynamical systems, Ph.D. Thesis, Department of Electrical Engineering, Stanford University, 1978.

64. W. Wasow, Asymptotic Expansions for Ordinary Differential Equations, Interscience, New York, 1965.

65. R. R. Wilde and P. K. Kokotivic, Optimal open and closed-loop control of singularly perturbed linear systems, IEEE Trans. Automatic Control, AC-18, (1973), 616-626.

66. J. H. Wilkinson, Note on the practical significance of the Drazin inverse, Nat. Physics Lab. Report, 1978.

67. K. T. Wong, The eigenvalue problem $\lambda Tx + Sx$, J. Diff. Eqn. 16(1974), 270-280.

68. K. D. Young, P. K. Kokotovic, and V. I. Utkin, A singular perturbation analysis of high-gain feedback systems, IEEE Trans. Automatic Control AC-22 (1977), 931-938.

Index

List of symbols

$\mathbb{C}$ complex numbers

$\mathbb{R}$ real numbers

$\mathbb{R}^n$, $(\mathbb{C}^n)$ real (complex) n-dimensional vectors, p. 4

$\mathbb{R}^{n\times m}$ $(\mathbb{C}^{n\times m})$, $n\times m$ real (complex) matrices

$\underline{x}$ vector

X matrix

$\|\underline{x}\|$ Euclidean norm, p. 4

$\|X\|$ matrix (operator) norm, p. 4

$(\underline{x},\underline{y})$ inner product, p. 4

M subspace, p. 5

$\oplus$ direct sum, p. 5

$P_{M,N}$, P_M projections, p. 5

$R(X)$ range of X (column space), p. 5

$N(X)$ null space of X, p. 5

X^* conjugate transpose

X^T transpose

$M^{\perp}$ orthogonal complement, p. 5

$\sigma(A)$ spectrum of A, p. 5

$\rho(A)$ spectral radius of A, p. 5

diag block diagonal matrix, p. 5

dim dimension, p. 5

det determinant

$X^{\dagger}$ Moore-Penrose inverse, p. 6

$W(A)$ numerical range of A, p. 6

$w(A)$ numerical radius of A, p. 6

Ind(X) Index of X, p. 7

X^D Drazin inverse of X, p. 8

exp exponential, p. 11

$\underline{x}^{(m)}$ m-th derivative

δ, $\delta^{(m)}$ delta functions, p. 14

$J[\underline{x},\underline{u}]$ cost functional, p. 19

$\underline{x}(0^-)$ left hand limit, p. 24

$\underline{x}(0^+)$ right hand limit

$\hat{A}$ p. 36

$L[\underline{f}]$ Laplace transform of $\underline{f}$

C^∞ infinitely differentiable functions, p. 71

$[A;B]$ $(I - B^DB)A(I - B^DB)$, p. 87

Re Real part, p. 88

Im Imaginary part, p. 88

$\rho(\Sigma,\Sigma')$ p. 88

$\dot{\underline{x}}$, $\dot{X}$ first derivative

$\ddot{\underline{x}}$, $\ddot{X}$ second derivative

$\Sigma_{ij}(\alpha)$ p. 123

A^o left inverse, p. 123

$S\{\alpha\}$ striped matrix, p. 123

$O(\cdot)$ order of

$[A,B]$ 2×1 block matrix, p. 143

$C^1[a,b]$ continuously differentiable functions on interval $[a,b]$

$\square$ end of proof mark (Halmos)